Formal Logic *

Paul Hoyningen-Huene

Formal Logic ✳ *A Philosophical Approach*

Translated by Alex Levine

University of Pittsburgh Press

Published by the University of Pittsburgh Press, Pittsburgh, Pa., 15261

Manufactured in the United States of America
Printed on acid-free paper
10 9 8 7 6 5 4 3 2 1

LIBRARY OF CONGRESS CATALOGING-IN-PUBLICATION DATA
Hoyningen-Huene, Paul, 1946–
    [Formale Logik. English]
    Formal logic : a philosophical approach / Paul Hoyningen-Huene ;
    translated by Alex Levine.
        p. cm.
    Includes bibliographical references (p.   ).
    ISBN 0-8229-5847-3 (alk. paper)
    1. Logic, Symbolic and mathematical—Textbooks. I. Title.
    BC135.H6913 2004
    160—c22
                        2003027966

Contents

Translator's Preface

This book differs in several respects from other introductory texts currently on the market. As the most important of these are canvassed in the author's preface, I see no need to comment on them further, except to note that the approach taken here is as unique among English-language treatments of logic as it is in the German-speaking world. But a few remarks on other features of this translation are perhaps in order.

I begin with a note on symbolic notation. Over the course of the late nineteenth and twentieth centuries, three major approaches to the symbolic representation of the formulas of first-order predicate logic were developed: the notations of Gottlob Frege's (1879) *Begriffschrift,* of Polish logician Jan Lukasiewicz, and of Giuseppe Peano, later revised by Bertrand Russell. Despite the undisputed importance of Frege's *Begriffschrift,* its cumbersome notational system never gained wider currency. Lukasiewicz's system, also known as "Polish notation," is in many respects the most economical (it dispenses with the need for parentheses). Its peculiar elegance makes it particularly suited to computational applications, where it has secured its own niche. But the overwhelming majority of logic texts, on both sides of the Atlantic, employ some variant or another of the Peano-Russell notation. None of the numerous variants, however, has attained the status of consensual standard.

This translation preserves the variant of Peano-Russell notation employed in the original German, one more common in Continental Europe than in the English-speaking world. The differences among the common notational variants are essentially trivial; anyone who has successfully mastered one of them should have little difficulty grasping any of the others. Still, the variant presented here has a few advantages. The most important of these is perhaps the resemblance between the symbolic representations for conjunction and disjunction ('∧' and '∨', respectively), and those for universal and existential quantifiers ('⋀' and '⋁'). This similarity serves to remind us of the respects in which predicate logic is a generalization of statement logic, thus easing the transition from the latter to the former. In any case, whenever a new symbol is introduced over the course of chapters 2 and 3, the common alternatives employed in other notational variants are always listed.

This translation incorporates several changes to the original text, all made in close consultation with the author, most of them too minor to mention. Several exercises have been changed, usually in deference to English colloquial usage, and corresponding changes have been made to appendix 2. Appendix 3, "Suggestions for Further Reading," lists several additional English-language texts. Most significant, a new section has been added to chapter 1 (section 3, "Validity and Soundness"). This section introduces the notion of logical soundness, applied to valid inferences with true premises. While this concept has no conventional name in German, it is a commonplace of English-language discussions of formal logic, and so the addition of this section was deemed necessary.

This translation has benefited greatly from the patience of Cynthia Miller at the University of Pittsburgh Press, and from the incomparable diligence and care of Paul Hoyningen-Huene, whose corrections to successive drafts have improved every page. He should not be blamed for any residual errors. I am immensely grateful for the support my colleagues in the Philosophy Department at Lehigh University have given this project. Finally, I owe an incalculable debt to Adriana Novoa.

Alex Levine, June 2003

Preface

The publication of a book entitled *Formal Logic: A Philosophical Approach* requires some justification. Surely by now there are quite enough introductions to logic, to mathematical logic, to the philosophy of logic, and to the logical tools required by particular disciplines, including philosophy. As is often the case, this book owes its existence to the author's frustration with earlier texts. Most texts in logic proper are written by logicians (usually of a mathematical stripe) or by logically or mathematically inclined philosophers. Such texts are primarily concerned with the development of a formal apparatus and its associated techniques. So-called philosophical problems are treated, at best, in passing. These approaches, in particular the more mathematically oriented of them, leave the connection between the arcane formalisms and the ordinary understanding of what logic is about almost entirely obscure. In more philosophical texts, by contrast, the philosophy of logic is frequently presented as a piece of residual philosophizing about issues for which technical solutions have long-since been devised, solutions that function flawlessly. Doing the philosophy of logic is thus a luxury, an indulgence that many expert logicians view with considerable skepticism.

In my view, what is missing is an attempt to unite the motives underlying both sorts of text. On the one hand, a philosophical approach to logic that fails to do justice to the formal niceties is clearly inadequate. On the other hand, even the advanced student frequently finds the more formally rigorous treatments full of puzzling, indeed seemingly arbitrary, steps— steps demanding far greater reflection and explanation than is usually provided. Clearly the present (short) book can only go a short distance in either direction toward uniting philosophical with formal motives. But I would like to show how an introduction to formal logic that gives proper consideration to the philosophical problems of logic might look. In the process, I hope to address some of the most common problems I have found to arise in logic classes designed for nonmathematicians. It strikes me that there are pedagogical advantages to be gained from linking philosophical with formal issues. I also aim to contribute both critically and constructively to the substantive explication of some of the more notorious quandaries of introductory logic, including the notions of logical form, material implication, and valid inference, as well as the so-called paradoxes of material implication, the circularity of attempts to justify logic itself, and the (in)adequacy of classical logic.

This book grew out of lectures I have given since 1976 at the Universities of Zurich, Berne, and Constance. The various ways in which those present at these lectures have understood, or occasionally misunderstood them, have served as a constant source of inspiration. Many of their suggestions have been incorporated. Dr. Gertrude Hirsch (formerly of the University of Zurich, now of the ETH Zurich, Switzerland, and the University of Constance, Germany) produced a creative transcription from recordings of lectures given during the winter term, 1983–84, thus paving the way for a book whose previous existence was confined to fragmentary handwritten notes. Christopher von Bülow of the University of Constance read several drafts with exacting attention, correcting the manuscript in countless matters of stylistic and substantive detail. He also contributed to the English version of appendix 2. Most of his suggestions were accepted. Over the years I have had numerous stimulating conversations on diverse logical problems, most notably with Prof. André Fuhrmann, formerly of the University of Constance and now at the Universidade São Judas Tadeu in São Paulo, Brazil; Prof. Gottfried Gabriel, formerly of the University of Constance and now at the University of Jena, Germany; Prof. Rolf George at University of Waterloo, Canada; Dr.

Stephen Read at the University of St. Andrews, United Kingdom; and Prof. Hans Rott, formerly of the University of Constance and now at the University of Regensburg, Germany. André Fuhrmann and Prof. Hubert Schleichert (University of Constance) generously provided me with the manuscripts of their own logic lectures, from which I took relatively little. Some of the exercises are indebted to the textbooks of Quine and von Savigny. Solutions to these exercises were prepared by Christopher von Bülow, who at one time served as my teaching assistant at the University of Constance, and were adapted for the English reader by Alex Levine. Cynthia Miller of Pittsburgh University Press oversaw the process of transforming a German book into an English one, which is an operation in many respects more complicated than initially expected. Finally, Alex Levine again did a splendid job of translating this book into English, which due to its particular style was not always easy. In addition, he made extremely useful suggestions on where to amend the text, even with respect to one of the proofs that turned out—much to my surprise—to be incomplete, and contributed the new section in chapter 1 on soundness. To all of the above, I extend my heartfelt thanks. Without their efforts, this book might have been completed much sooner—but it would have been much worse.

Paul Hoyningen-Huene, Hannover, July 2003

Formal Logic *

1 ✳ **Introduction**

1. An Example

This chapter introduces the subject of formal logic. Toward this end it seems natural to begin with a definition, one that explains what formal logic is. This is the normal practice in teaching a whole range of specialized fields, but in philosophy a definition is usually a false start, at least it is if we take the definition seriously and plan to stick to it. A definition determines how the thing being defined is to be understood. In philosophy, however, we must first come to some preliminary understanding of the thing (in some broad sense of the word 'thing'), an understanding that is then critically explored and perhaps altered. For this purpose, the device of the initial definition, held constant through all subsequent discussion, is ill suited.

In philosophy, we generally start out with some prior knowledge of the subject under study, albeit not the sort of knowledge we really want. Frequently, we find our subject somehow implicit in some more-or-less concrete fact or example. The analysis of such examples is thus an extremely useful way of approaching the subject itself. In this way we shall approach one of the central notions of formal logic, the notion of valid inference. As to why this notion is central to formal logic, and why this logic is called "formal," these are questions we cannot yet answer. But our analysis of examples will get us started in the right direction.

I begin with an example of the familiar, trivial variety so often employed in logic:

Example 1.1   All logicians are human

All humans need sleep

*

Therefore,   All logicians need sleep

To simplify our discussion of this and future examples, we will call the sentences above the asterisk "premises" and the sentence below it the "conclusion." Being a premise or a conclusion is clearly not a property of a sentence in and of itself—it is merely a function of whether a given sentence is found above or below the asterisk. Now, in this case the move from premises to conclusion is somehow compelling, and so we call the whole a (logically) valid inference. It is of the utmost importance to realize that the expression "valid inference" refers to the entire system of three sentences and not merely to the conclusion. In other words, validity is a feature of the relationship between premises and conclusion and is not a property of the conclusion itself. Of course there are things that *can* be said about the conclusion, such as that it is true, but then we are not talking about the inference, which again is the particular relationship between premises and conclusion. I will return to this distinction in greater detail below (see II.2.4.b), but for now suffice it to insist that the following are two separate questions:

1. Is the inference valid?
2. Is the conclusion true?

(The ease with which we confuse these questions is due to the fact that there is, after all, a connection between the validity of an inference and the truth of its conclusion; I will return to this later.) As we shall see, the distinction between these two questions is central to logic.

It is a truly remarkable fact that one rarely encounters anyone who fails to agree that Example 1.1 constitutes a logically valid inference, in the sense that the transition from premises to conclusion is somehow compelling. Without having to come to any agreement, or demand any sort of explanation, anyone with sufficient mastery of the English language to understand the sentences in question recognizes the inference as valid. We would be hard pressed to find someone who, having accepted the premises, would refuse to accept the conclusion. It is worth asking why this is so. At this stage, however, I cannot pursue this question. Let us extract five features of logically valid inferences from our example. Anyone who accepts Example 1.1 as logically valid will also be prepared to ascribe all of these features to it and to related inferences.

Feature 1.   When the premises are true, then the conclusion is also true.

Here we must pay close attention to what is being said. We are not claiming *that the premises are true,* but only that *if* they are true, *then* the conclusion is also true. This feature holds with all logically valid inferences and thus deserves a name. I shall call it the "truth-transferring" property of logically valid inferences. So, when the premises of a logically valid inference happen to be true, the conclusion is also true—the truth of the premises is *transferred* to the conclusion.[1]

This truth-transferring quality of our example is, in the end, something one must see for oneself; anyone incapable of seeing it will never understand what logic is all about. Thus, as far as this fundamental insight into truth transfer is concerned, logic cannot be taught. To be sure, I can hint and gesture toward the insight, toward the experience of a certain thought process, with some degree of clarity. But no such descriptions of the relevant thought process will serve as a set of instructions such that, if one only follows the recipe, one will come to understand what truth transfer is. Experience of the thought process in question cannot be replaced by descriptions of it, and this experience is fundamental to logic. In this

---

1. Here the limitations of the truth transfer metaphor become apparent. When funds are transferred from account *A* to account *B,* they are obviously no longer in account *A.* By contrast, successful truth transfer from premises to conclusion does not mean that the premises are no longer true (provided they were true in the first place). Furthermore, in our present example, the conclusion "All logicians need sleep" is true anyway. No "transfer" of truth from the premises is required in order to make it true.

regard, our situation is far from unique. There are other experiences for which no description can be substituted, such as the experience of being in love, of the effects of alcohol, or of swimming in a strong current. Here, too, only someone who has had the right sort of experience will understand what the discussion is about.

> *Feature 2.*   The truth of the premises plays no role in our assessment of the validity of the inference.

Here it is claimed that the validity of an inference cannot be judged on the basis of the truth of its premises. Before defending this assertion, which may strike some as implausible, I hasten to point out that this second feature is not inconsistent with the first. Feature 1 is a claim about what happens *when* the premises are true; it does not assert *that* the premises are true. Now for the defense of Feature 2: Let us substitute the expression 'have characteristic *S*' for the expression 'need sleep' wherever the latter occurs in Example 1.1. This yields:

> *Example 1.2.*   All logicians are human.
>   All humans have characteristic *S*.
>
>   *
>
> Therefore,   All logicians have characteristic *S*.

As is plain to see, we have another logically valid inference before us. But it must also be noted that the sentences 'All humans have characteristic *S*' and 'All logicians have characteristic *S*' are not straightforwardly true or false statements. For the meaning of the expression 'characteristic *S*' is indeterminate, thus leaving the two sentences in which it occurs equally indeterminate. Nonetheless, the logical validity of Example 1.2 may be seen without the slightest difficulty, even more easily than the validity of Example 1.1. Example 1.2 thus demonstrates that our assessment of the validity of an inference cannot depend on the truth of its premises, for in this example the second premise is so indeterminate as to be neither true nor false. Accordingly, ascertaining the validity of Example 1.1 does not require that we consult the Institute for Sleep Study on the distribution of sleep requirements among various segments of the population. The truth of the premises of this earlier example is equally irrelevant to its validity.

Indeed, the premises might be manifestly false without undermining the validity of the inference. This can easily be demonstrated by substituting the expression 'have characteristic S' as it occurs in Example 1.2 with some other expression that makes the second premise false (for example, 'are reptiles'). Now, one might be tempted to suppose that it is impossible to validly infer anything from false premises, but this temptation must be resisted. Arguments of the following form are, after all, commonplace: "Let us assume that all humans are reptiles. Under this assumption, what would logicians be?" In mathematics, inferences drawn from false premises are systematically employed in a procedure known as indirect proof, in which we assume the exact opposite of what we are trying to prove and infer a contradiction from it. This contradictory consequence shows that our assumption is false and thus that its opposite, the claim we were out to prove in the first place, must be true (for a more detailed exposition of indirect proof, see section II.2.4.f).

Feature 3.   From any valid inference, many additional valid inferences may be generated (mechanically).

The procedure by which these additional inferences are generated has actually already put in an appearance, in our explication of Feature 2. Simply replace such expressions as 'logician', 'human,' and 'need sleep' as they occur in Example 1.1 with other expressions, such as 'animal', 'life form', and 'God's creation', respectively. Our replacements must be methodical, in the sense that for *every* occurrence of an expression being replaced, we replace it with *one and the same* new expression; otherwise, our procedure will fail to generate further valid inferences. The substitution proposed above thus yields:

Example 1.3.   All animals are life forms.

All life forms are God's creations.

*

Therefore,   All animals are God's creations.

This inference, too, is logically valid, as should be immediately clear. In this instance, the procedure of replacing each and every occurrence of a given expression with an occurrence of one and the same new expression has thus yielded a new valid inference. But of course this success hardly justifies the claim made in Feature 3, since it remains conceivable that the same procedure might fail for other examples. However, consideration of the fourth feature should persuade us that, in fact, our procedure will *always* yield new valid inferences.

Feature 4.   The meanings of the expressions occurring in an inference are irrelevant to its validity.

The above formulation of Feature 4 is provisional and somewhat imprecise. By way of clarification, we return to Example 1.1, this time replacing every occurrence of 'logician', 'human', and 'need sleep' by A, B, and C, respectively, yielding:

Example 1.4.   All As are Bs.

All Bs are Cs.

*

Therefore,   All As are Cs.

Once again, as with Example 1.2, we observe the logical validity of this inference, this despite the fact that A, B, and C are completely indeterminate. It follows that logically valid inference has nothing to do with word meaning, for the validity of an inference can be detected even after certain expressions ('logician', 'human', etc.) have been replaced with single letters. The "mechanism" of a valid inference thus depends not on the particular expressions it contains, but on something else. We will return to this something else later.

Having performed the abstraction procedure involved in converting Example 1.1 into Example 1.4, we begin to understand why Features 1–3 really *are* features of valid inferences. Feature 1 asserts that any valid inference is such that if its premises are true, then its conclusion is also true. In establishing the validity of Example 1.4, we consider this: if all *A*s are *B*s, and if all *B*s are also *C*s, is it then the case that all *A*s are *C*s? This question in essence asks whether the inference is truth-transferring—whether the truth of the premises is transferred to the conclusion. We can answer it in the affirmative without having the slightest idea what it would mean for all *A*s to be *B*s or all *B*s to be *C*s, let alone whether both claims—both premises—are actually true. But this is precisely what Feature 2 asserts of valid inferences. This result further underscores the possibility of using any valid inference to generate further valid inferences (Feature 3), for since the meanings of constituent expressions are irrelevant to the validity of the inference, they may be replaced with new expressions, provided we always replace each original expression with one and the same substitute. This reasoning establishes that Features 1–3 are implicit in Feature 4. Anyone who follows this reasoning is well on his or her way to grasping what logic is all about.

It should be noted that in our various manipulations of Example 1.1 we have played around with several of its constituent expressions, but not with all of them. For example, we have always left the word 'all' unchanged. Now let us see what happens when we replace the word 'all', as it occurs in Example 1.4, with the word 'some'. This substitution yields:

Example 1.5.   Some *A*s are *B*s
              Some *B*s are *C*s
              *
Therefore,   Some *A*s are *C*s

Is this inference valid, in the sense that the truth of the premises guarantees the truth of the conclusion? To simplify, let us replace '*A*', '*B*', and '*C*' by particular meaningful expressions. If Example 1.5 is valid, then by

Feature 4, the result of this replacement should also be a valid inference. Let us substitute 'plant', 'meat-eater', and 'cat' for *'A'*, *'B'*, and *'C'* respectively. This yields:

Example 1.6.   Some plants are meat-eaters.

Some meat-eaters are cats.

               *

Therefore,   Some plants are cats.

This conclusion is obviously false. But since both premises are true, their truth cannot have been transferred to the conclusion. The inference is thus not valid. Any inference that fails the test of validity is called "invalid."

*_Exercise 1.1._ Find other examples, analogous to 1.6, that demonstrate the invalidity of 1.5.

*_Exercise 1.2._ Find expressions which, when inserted into Example 1.5, yield true premises *and* a true conclusion. How can such examples be reconciled with the invalidity of the inference?

*_Exercise 1.3._ Let the claim "Some *As* are *Bs*" be represented by the following diagram:

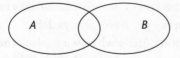

Now let "All *As* are *Bs*" be represented by the following diagram:

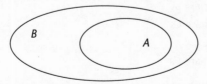

Using these diagrams, explain why Example 1.4 constitutes a valid inference while 1.5 is invalid. Then analyze your solution to Exercise 1.2 by means of similar diagrams.

It has thus emerged that in a valid inference, such as Example 1.1, expressions like 'human', 'need sleep', and the like play a different role from expressions like 'all' (or 'some'). Expressions of the first type can be replaced by other such expressions without affecting the validity of the inference (provided each occurrence of a given expression is always replaced by an occurrence of the same replacement). On the other hand, expressions of the second type cannot be so replaced; the validity of the inference depends on them. I will call this observation the fifth feature of valid inferences, noting that our formulation of Feature 5, like that of Feature 4, will have to be provisional:

Feature 5.   The validity or invalidity of inferences depends on such
expressions as 'all' and 'some'.

＊*Exercise 1.4.* Formulate a valid inference containing the expression 'some'
and three other expressions (or letters).

2. Preliminary Remarks on the Notion of Logical Form

The notion of logical form, to which we now turn, is of central importance to logic. Before going any further, I must first explain what we mean to achieve by introducing it. As we have just seen, the validity of an inference does not depend on every constituent expression in its component statements. On the contrary, the meanings of many such expressions, such as 'logician', 'human', and 'need sleep' in Example 1.1, are irrelevant to its validity. Any component of a statement that *does* contribute to the validity of inferences containing that statement is said to belong to the *logical form of the statement.* By contrast, any component of a statement that remains irrelevant to the validity of inferences containing the statement will be consigned to the *(logical) content of the statement.* For a preliminary explication of this distinction, we turn once again to Example 1.1. As we have seen, in the first premise, "All logicians are human," while the meanings of 'logician' and 'human' were irrelevant to the subsequent inference, the same was not true for 'all'. The logical form of this statement might thus be rendered as 'All *A*s are *B*s'. Similarly, 'Some *A*s are *B*s' is a good candidate for the logical form of 'Some textbooks are exciting'. It thus appears that the move from Example 1.1 to Example 1.4 is just a matter of focusing in on logical forms for the constituent statements, where everything irrelevant to the validity of the inference has been stripped away from 1.4.

Our aim in introducing the notion of logical form will thus be to allow us to isolate exactly those components of statements that are relevant to the validity of inferences in which the statements occur. Success here will allow us to assess the validity of a given inference by reference only to the logical forms of its constituent statements, without having to engage with their contents. I hasten to point out that up to now I have merely articulated the main reason for wanting a notion of logical form, without doing more than gesturing toward the notion itself. It will not be properly introduced until sections II.1.2, and II.1.2. For the present, I content myself with four remarks on logical form.

1. The logical form of a sentence is obtained by *abstracting from the content* of the sentence. This is a straightforward consequence of our preliminary observations. "Abstraction" comes from the Latin *abstrahere,* meaning "to pull away" or "remove." What is removed from a sentence is its content, and what is left is its logical form. This process draws a sharp line through a sentence. On one side of this line are the parts belonging to logical form; those on the other side belong to content. Graphic as this description is, by itself it remains indeterminate, for we need to know *precisely where to draw this line.* To say that we draw the line between form and content is plainly insufficient. Why, one might rejoin, should the 'all' in "All humans need sleep" belong to logical form rather than content? There are other sorts of lines one can draw between the forms and contents of sentences, as, for example, in grammar. There are several ways to abstract a grammatical form from the sentence "All humans need sleep." Abstracting by syntactic components, we have modifier ('all'), subject

('humans'), predicate ('need'), direct object ('sleep'). Or we might focus instead on the parts of speech, observing that the sentence is composed of an indefinite pronoun ('all'), two nouns ('humans' and 'sleep'), and a verb ('need'). If we prefer, we can entirely abstract away word meanings to consider only the length of the sentence, expressed in the number of words. Finally, we might abstract by syntactic structure, in which case we would find that the sentence consists of a single independent clause.

As these examples plainly illustrate, there are many ways to turn our sentence into an abstraction. In each case, what is being *abstracted away* may be called the content of the sentence, and what is left over may be called its form. In order to target a *particular* form/content distinction, we must specify *precisely where the line between form and content should be drawn*. This specification will depend, in turn, on the exact nature of the task our form/content distinction is designed to perform. In ignorance of this task, the call for a form/content distinction remains vacuous. Proper attention to our reason for introducing the notion of logical form in the first place is thus indispensable to any real understanding of formal logic: motivated by our desire to analyze the logical validity of inferences, the notion of logical form allows us to isolate those aspects of sentences that are relevant to the validity of inferences in which those sentences occur. The somewhat less common designation of "(logical) content" applies to everything else.

2. But even when we confine ourselves to the logical form of a sentence, there is still more than one way to draw the line between form and content. The basis for this ambiguity will be treated with greater care later. For now, suffice it to say that any reference to *the* logical form of a sentence must be viewed with suspicion, for every sentence has more than one logical form. There are different subfields of logic, each of which is characterized by its own particular distinction between logical form and content. For our purposes, two kinds of logical form are of primary importance. I will call these "statement form" (see II.1.2) and "predicate form" (see III.1.2). Statement logic is characterized by the notion of state-

ment form, and predicate logic, by the notion of predicate form. We should thus avoid talking about *the* logical form of a sentence as if there were a single, unambiguous form, for even when the context is rich enough to make it clear which notion is meant, this manner of speaking still leaves us with the mistaken sense that there is some unequivocal notion to be had. Even within a particular area of logic in which the notion of logical form is well defined, there is often more than one logical form of a given statement (see II.1.2.b and III.1.2.b).

3. If we plan to work with logical forms, and thus seek to remove everything from a sentence that does not belong to one of its logical forms, we need a way of representing the forms themselves. Aristotle (384–322 B.C.), the founder of formal logic, developed a *symbol system* for representing a particular class of logical forms. Representations of logical forms by means of such symbol systems are called "formulas." Incidentally, I have already tacitly introduced Aristotle's symbol system in Examples 1.4 and 1.5, in which particular expressions were replaced by letters (for example, 'logician' by *A*). Our cultural heritage is such that this procedure is almost completely transparent. We recall our algebra classes, in which all of us, with varying degrees of pleasure, learned how to work with letters in place of numbers. In algebra, as in logic, formulas represent the forms of statements: specifically, mathematical statements (see II.1.2.b, No. 9). But the relative ease with which we handle formulas should not lead us to underestimate the considerable intellectual effort involved in introducing the form/content distinction for logical forms and in developing appropriate symbol systems with which to represent them.

4. By now it should be clear what we mean by formal logic. Logic is primarily concerned with the study of logically valid inference and related notions and processes. Toward this end, there is no need to consider sentences in their entirety—it suffices to capture their logical forms. Incidentally, the name "formal logic" was not coined by Aristotle but by Immanuel Kant (1724–1804) in 1781 in his *Critique of Pure Reason* (1st German ed., p. 131; 2d ed., p. 170). Before Kant, formal logic was known

simply as "logic" or occasionally as "dialectic." Kant believed that traditional logic could be supplemented by a new kind of logic concerned with the very content from which formal logic sought to remove itself. For reasons that need not concern us here, Kant called this new field "transcendental logic," reserving the name "formal logic" for traditional logic as it had been known up to then.

3. Validity and Soundness

As should be clear from the preceding section, this text is concerned with questions of logical form, not content. And no formal notion is more important than that of logical validity. But our motives in seeking to understand this formal notion should be acknowledged: the reason we are so keen on validity is not just that we are interested in knowing when the truth of our premises guarantees the truth of a conclusion. Frequently, what we most want to know about a given argument or inference is, *is the conclusion true*? Knowing when an inference is valid can help us to answer this question, but it is not the whole story. Compare Example 1.1 with the following:

Example 1.7.   All logicians are reptiles.
All reptiles need sleep.
*
Therefore,   All logicians need sleep.

Example 1.8.   All logicians are reptiles.
All reptiles are Martians.
*
All logicians are Martians.

Now, as established by our analysis of Example 1.4, it is plain that 1.1, 1.7, and 1.8 all have identical logical forms. Validity being a feature of inference form, it follows that all three are equally valid. However, it is quite obvious that they do not succeed equally well in persuading us of the truth of their respective conclusions.

The primary difference between 1.1, 1.7, and 1.8 lies in the truth of their premises. Example 1.1 contains two true premises, whereas only one premise of 1.7 is true (the second), and both premises of 1.8 are false. Additionally, 1.7 and 1.8 differ in their conclusions. The conclusion of 1.7 is true, despite the falsehood of the first premise, and the conclusion of 1.8 is false. But to reiterate, all three inferences have exactly the same logical form; they are all equally valid. Indeed, a valid argument can have true premises and a true conclusion (1.1), false premises and a true conclusion (1.7), or false premises and a false conclusion (1.8). For that matter, an *invalid* inference can have true premises and a true conclusion! The only combination ruled out by the very notion of validity is that of a valid inference with true premises and false conclusion, since a valid inference is one for which the logical forms of premises and conclusion guarantee that whenever the former are true, so is the latter.

The usual way of drawing the distinction between 1.1 on the one hand and 1.7 and 1.8 on the other is to say that 1.1 (but neither 1.7 nor 1.8) is a *sound* inference. There are two parts to being a sound inference. A sound inference must be valid. In addition, it must have all true premises. From the understanding of validity gained in I.1, it follows that any inference that meets both conditions for soundness *must* have a true conclusion. For the fact that the inference is valid makes it truth-transferring, guaranteeing that if its premises are true, then its conclusion must also be true. But a sound inference is a valid inference with all true premises, so the truth of its conclusion may be taken as given.

Unlike validity, soundness is not a purely formal notion. Whether an argument is sound has to do not only with the logical forms of premises and conclusions, but also with whether or not the premises are true. On the other hand, soundness is not strictly a matter of logical content, either. It is worth noting that the soundness of an inference can be assessed without knowing the meanings of either the premises or the conclusion. The only information we need in order to tell whether a given valid inference is also sound is whether the premises are true. To anticipate a notion introduced in Definition 1.2 below, all we need to know is the truth values of the premises. Thus, while soundness is not purely a matter of form, it is hardly a matter of content. Soundness is a mixed notion.

4. Statements, Primitive Statements, and Compound Statements

Truth transfer, as we have seen, is the central feature of logically valid inference (See I.1, Feature 1): When the premises of a valid inference are true, its conclusion is also true. But such talk of truth transfer would make no sense unless it was at least *possible* for the sentences in the premises and the conclusion to *be* true. It thus behooves us to distinguish those sentences that *can* be true (or false) from those that lack this feature. This is the first of three distinctions, which will ultimately lead us into statement and predicate logic.

4.1. Sentences and Statements

Are there sentences that are neither true nor false? Note that I am not here asking whether we in fact *know* a given sentence is true or false, but whether it always even makes sense to ascribe truth or falsehood to a sentence. But now observe that the first sentence of this very paragraph is an example of a sentence to which neither truth nor falsehood can be meaningfully attributed, for the sentence "Are there sentences that are neither true nor false?" is a question. In addition to questions, some sentences express norms (No turn on red!), desires (I would really like better weather tomorrow!), demands (Drop by this evening!), commands (Stand still!), and exclamations (Oh, if only Christmas could come sooner!). None of these is either true or false. This is not to say that there are not other criteria by which we evaluate such sentences—for example, as appropriate or shameless, modest or immodest, well posed or poorly posed, etc.—but they simply cannot be judged true or false. To a first approximation, it appears that only those sentences used to assert something can be true or false, and this is not what questions, commands, exclamations, and the like are for. (This is only a first approximation, since it leaves out two classes of statements, which, despite the fact that they are true or false, cannot be used to assert anything. See II.2.2.a and II.2.3.) In the part of logic concerned with truth-transferring inferences, which includes both statement and predicate logic, we must thus begin by excluding all sentences that *cannot* be either true or false. This does not mean that there is no appropriate logical treatment for such sentences, as in the logic of interrogatives or the logic of imperatives, only that we will not be dealing with them here. The following definition pins down the class of sentences with which statement and predicate logic are concerned.

Definition 1.1. A *statement* (or *veridical sentence*) is a sentence that is either true or false.

A few remarks are in order.

1. First of all, it will be helpful to introduce a standard logical convention. For this purpose, we will move right to a second definition:

Definition 1.2. In logic, "True" and "False" are called "truth values."

As abbreviations for these values we will use T for "True" and F for "False." One sometimes encounters other abbreviations, such as 1 for "True" and 0 for "False." This alternative device is particularly useful in the analysis of logic gates in circuitry and in computer science in general. The expression "truth value" was introduced by the German logician Gottlob Frege (1848–1925), one of the founders of modern formal logic. Frege saw that it was possible to construe "True" and "False" as the *values* of particular functions (see chap. 4).

2. Definition 1.1 is concerned with sentences that are either true or false, and not with sentences for which it is necessarily possible for us to *determine* whether they are true or false. This distinction is extremely important in logic, as in other fields. For it is one thing to say that a sentence

has the quality of being either true or false and quite another to actually determine which it is. *Having* a truth value is a necessary (but not sufficient) condition for the possibility of our *discovering* truth or falsehood, as we cannot determine a truth value when no such truth value is present. But there are sentences for which, although we can be certain that they have a truth value, there is nonetheless no possible effective procedure for determining the value in question. Consider, for example, the statements with which we articulate natural laws. Such universal statements are purported to hold for all possible instances of a given kind, and yet there is no way to test them for all such instances. Yet despite the fundamental obstacles facing any attempt to establish their truth value, statements of natural laws are supposed to be unequivocally true or false.

3. Definition 1.1 should be understood as merely a *stipulative convention governing our use of the word 'statement,'* and *not* as a substantive claim about all sentences that attempt to assert something. In point of fact, in ordinary usage we often assess the truth values of statements as indefinite, an assessment ruled out by Definition 1.1. According to this definition, every statement is either true or false—there is no third possibility. This insistence on the exclusivity and exhaustiveness of our two truth values is known as the "principle of the excluded middle"—in Latin, *tertium non datur* (no third is given). But for a great many sentences, which we would not hesitate to classify as statements in the ordinary sense, neither of our two acceptable truth values seems appropriate. In general, there seem to be two sorts of reasons for this failure. First, some statements are so vague as to make an ascription of truth value impossible or at least highly problematic. Consider the following:

Example 1.9. Fred is tall.

Now if Fred is over 6′6″, the statement is clearly true, but what if he is only 6′3″, 6′2″, or 5′10″? Here the problem is less a matter of *determining* the truth value of 'Fred is tall'; it is rather a question of whether the statement even *has* truth value (see Remark 2 above). For sentences such as 1.9, a separate brand of logic has been developed that allows for three truth values: truth, falsity, and indeterminacy. In many respects, it is an extension of the sort of logic with which we are here concerned.

A second reason for questioning the universal applicability of the principle of the excluded middle to all statements may be found in the analysis of statements about future events, including the following:

> *Example 1.10.* The numbers in the next lottery drawing will be 2, 9, 11, 18, 21, and 35.

To claim, as the principle of the excluded middle requires, that it is *now* the case that this statement is either true or false is to commit oneself to the claim that there is already a fact of the matter as to whether this particular sequence of numbers will be drawn or not. But this is to assert that *all future events are already determined.* This view is called "determinism." It now appears that unconditional acceptance of the principle of the excluded middle would commit us to determinism! But regardless of whether we wish to be determinists or not, it seems high-handed to force implicit acceptance of determinism on grounds of a definition in formal logic. It is for this reason that I began this remark by recommending that Definition 1.1 be viewed as merely a stipulative convention on our use of the word 'statement' within those branches of logic with which we are here concerned: classical statement and predicate logic. 'Statement' is thus defined as a technical term specific to statement and predicate logic, and as such we should expect its use to deviate from ordinary speech, just as the technical use of 'force' in physics deviates from everyday uses of the same term.

4. From this perspective, Definition 1.1 appears innocuous, as it merely fixes the meaning of the word 'statement' for purposes of statement and predicate logic. Implicit within this definition, however, we find one of the fundamental problems of logic. We are told that statements are the sorts of things that can be true or false—but what *are* these things, exactly? At present, there appear to be at least five sorts of answer, each with its own variants:

a. Is the *assertion* made by a given statement a purely physical process or object, such as a datable acoustic blast (a speech act) or a particular, concrete inscription? If so, then a statement would be a unique, unrepeatable event or object in space and time. Such items are called "tokens."

b. Or perhaps a statement is an *assertion template,* an abstract pattern of sounds or written symbols, capable of numerous distinct instantiations. On this account, a statement is not a token; it is a *type.*

c. Then again, we might choose to focus on the *act of judgment,* on the mental activity taking place within the subject who entertains a given statement. In even more distinguished vocabulary, this would mean treating the statement as a contingent attribute of consciousness. Once again, the statement becomes a spatiotemporally unique, unrepeatable event, a token.

d. A still further possibility would be to consider the *judgment template,* the abstract type of which particular acts of judgment are the tokens.

e. Finally, we might target the *meaning* (or *sense*) expressed by the statement, sometimes also called *the stated* or *the intended facts* (expressed by the statement in question), *the contents of judgment, the thought,* or *the proposition.* In which case, we must ask, to what extent and in what sense do these meanings, facts, propositions, etc. exist in relation to the four sorts of entities listed in a–d?

Needless to say, this list merely scratches the surface of the underlying problem. For even if there were deciding arguments in favor of one of the five possibilities, the attempt to elaborate the favored alternative would doubtless give rise to its own host of difficulties.

The problem of trying to determine what a statement actually is, for purposes of logic, is not a problem that arises merely out of some infelicity in the formulation of Definition 1.1; thus it is not one we can dispel by simply reformulating or perhaps omitting this definition—though in doing so the problem might be disguised. The problem here has to do with the very nature of statements, what we might call the "bearers" of truth or falsehood, and as such it is intrinsic to our subject. Since we are concerned with that part of logic that deals with statements and their relations to one another, this problem is an inevitable part of our attempts to understand what logic is really about. And as the problem has turned out to be particularly difficult and multifaceted, we should acknowledge right from the start that the foundations of logic rest on shaky ground. But as is frequently (though not always!) the case in both philosophy and the sciences, this foundational instability does not preclude our pragmatic engagement with our subject. In logic, as it happens, we are able to develop very precise notions of logical form, along with techniques for checking the validity of inferences, without this fundamental problem of the nature of statements getting in the way. Indeed, the mathematical approach to logic (see IV.2) provides us with a perspective from which it is possible to abstract from the problem entirely. As far as the formal aspect of logic is concerned, we can thus leave open the question of what logic is really about. But the question remains and must eventually be addressed by anyone whose interest in logic goes beyond the purely technical. I will return to it briefly in II.3.2.

5. In what follows, we will encounter many examples of statements, all of which must be assumed to clearly satisfy Definition 1.1, despite the difficulties cited above. Merely *attempting* to do justice to these problems would leave even our simplest examples intractably long and complicated. Instead, in invoking such examples as 'The apartment is nice,' we will simply take them as statements in the sense of Definition 1.1. Of course, strictly speaking this sentence is extraordinarily vague. Not only does it not specify *which* apartment is meant, it also fails to restrict itself to a particular timeframe. Nor does it provide any criteria for the niceness of apartments. There will thus be numerous contexts in which the truth value of this sentence remains indeterminate. But from now on we will read this and similar examples either as having been appropriately expanded or as having been used only in appropriately restricted contexts, such that they have determinate truth value.

❋*Exercise 1.5.* Given Definition 1.1, which of the following sentences are statements?

> 1. Oh my gosh!
> 2. I haven't the slightest intention of considering your offer.
> 3. And if they haven't died yet, they're still alive today.
> 4. Let *n* be any natural number.
> 5. Proceed to Park Place.
> 6. $200 fine for unauthorized parking.
> 7. You have no idea how silly you look.
> 8. If this goes on, it'll drive me crazy.
> 9. This statement is false.
> 10. Which of the above sentences are statements?

4.2. Primitive and Compound Statements

Next we divide the entire domain of statements into those that are *composed of further statements* and those that are *not composed of further statements.* The reason for introducing this distinction will become clear later on, when it emerges as an important tool in the analysis of certain classes of inferences. Consider the following example:

> *Example 1.11.* The apartment is nice and it is fairly expensive.

This statement is composed of two separable component statements: 'The apartment is nice', and 'The apartment is fairly expensive'. They are joined into a single statement by the conjunction 'and.' Example 1.12 is similarly structured:

> *Example 1.12.* Anthony is reading a logic book, because he finds logic incredibly exciting.

Here the two component statements are 'Anthony is reading a logic book' and 'Anthony finds logic incredibly exciting', now joined by the conjunction 'because'. We call both examples *compound* statements and say that they are composed of *primitive* statements.

Three further remarks are in order. First, it is worth noting that, in addition to such conjunctions as 'and' and 'because', the English language contains other devices that smooth the process of constructing compound statements. For instance, in 1.12, the subject of the second component statement ('Anthony') has been replaced by a pronoun ('he'). Second, the conjunctions 'and' and 'because', along with other expressions by means of which primitive statements are joined to form compound statements, are called "sentential connectives" or simply "connectives" (see I.4.3 and II.1.1 below). Finally, what we call "primitive" statements are primitive only in the very specific sense that they are not composed of other *statements*. But in another sense, such statements are also compounds; like (nearly) all statements, they are composed of several words. In logic, such primitive statements are also called "atomic statements." This label should not, however, mislead anyone into thinking that atomic statements are always really, really tiny, like the atoms of which matter is composed. The Greek root *atomos* simply means "indivisible" (although physical atoms have turned out to be divisible, a discovery which—thank God!—need not concern us here).

※*Exercise 1.6.* Which of the following compound sentences are statements?

1. If you come back, may God have mercy on your soul.
2. Hopefully you'll be doing well next time.
3. If Fred goes out with Anne, then I think Sarah will be angry.
4. It is indeed true that one candidate won the popular vote while the other won the office.
5. Someone recently asked me whether I lived in New York or Philadelphia.
6. Wait, that's not right—or maybe it is?

4.3. Extensional vs. Intensional Connectives

Having distinguished primitive (or atomic) from compound statements, we now proceed to divide the connectives by which compound statements are joined into two classes. Compound statements joined by members of the first class all have in common the fact that their truth values *depend only on the truth values of their constituent primitive statements.* We say that the truth values of such compound statements depend only on the *truth values* of their constituent primitive statements, so as to make it clear that the truth values of the compounds *do not* depend on the *meanings* of the constituent primitive statements. Consider Example 1.11: "The apartment is nice and it is fairly expensive." To determine the truth value of the statement, it suffices to know the truth values of the two constituent primitive statements. If both are true, the compound statement is true; if one or both are false, the compound statement is false, for it simultaneously asserts the truth of both primitive statements. The connective 'and' is thus a member of this first class, in that it appears possible to determine the truth values of compound statements joined by this expression by reference only to the truth values of the constituent primitive statements. Neither the meanings of these statements nor any other circumstances need be taken into account.

The same does not hold for the second class of connectives. The truth values of compound statements joined by such connectives do not depend *only* on the truth values of the constituent primitive statements. Consider Example 1.12: "Anthony is reading a logic book, because he finds logic incredibly exciting." Let us suppose that Anthony actually is reading a logic book, and let us suppose further that Anthony really does find logic incredibly exciting. Let it be given, in other words, that both of the primitive statements in Example 1.12 are true. Does this information, by itself, tell us the truth value of the compound statement? Of course, the compound statement *might* be true, if the statement accurately accounts for the motives behind Anthony's choice of reading material. But it might as easily be false—as it would be, for example, if Anthony is doing his reading on Christmas Eve, not because he finds it so exciting (though he does), but in order to kill time while waiting to open his presents the following morning. So with connectives like 'because' it is usually not possible to read the truth value of the compound statement off the truth values of its constituent primitive statements. More information is needed.

The distinction between these two classes of connectives is expressed in the following definition:

> *Definition 1.3* 1. *Extensional* (or *truth-functional*) connectives are such that the truth values of compound statements joined by these connectives are completely determined by the truth values of the constituent primitive statements.
>
> 2. *Intensional* connectives are such that the truth values of compound statements joined by these connectives are not determined by the truth values of the constituent primitive statements alone.
>
> *∗Exercise 1.7.* Which of the following connectives are truth-functional: 'or', 'due to the fact that', and 'if . . . then'.

Definition 1.3 introduces some novel terminology. The extensional connectives are called "truth-functional" because the truth values of the compound statements joined by them can be viewed as a *function* of the truth values of the constituent primitive statements. In general, to say that y is a function of x means that the value of variable y is unequivocally determined by the value of variable x. "Intensional" comes from "intension," which refers to the meaning of a sentence, and "extensional" means simply "independent of the meaning of a sentence."

Once again, proper appreciation of the above distinctions will have to await our development of statement logic in the following chapter.

5. Review

The following will suffice as a provisional summary of this introduction to the central issue of formal logic. Formal logic is primarily concerned with valid inferences—in other words, with inferences in which the logical forms of premises and conclusion force us to accept the latter once we have accepted the former. More generally, formal logic deals with those features of statements, and of the relationships between statements, that may be said to hold *by virtue of the logical forms* of the statements in question. Valid inference is an example of such a relationship, and logical truth, about which we will learn more later, will be an example of such a feature. Our discussion has presupposed the sort of prior understanding required in order to evaluate basic inferences as valid or invalid, several examples about which were analyzed. Over the course of several sequential steps, I motivated the introduction of a notion of logical form. Finally, we paved the way for a proper treatment of statement and predicate logic with the following distinctions: statements versus sentences in general; compound versus primitive statements; and extensional versus intensional connectives. We turn now to a detailed discussion of the extensional connectives and their properties.

2 ✳ Statement Logic

Statement logic, to which we now turn, is sometimes also called "sentential logic" or "propositional logic." The rationale behind the first of these alternative names is clear enough, since statements are a kind of sentence. As for the second, the meanings of statements are, for various reasons, sometimes stipulated to be independent of the statements themselves, in which case it is said that a statement expresses a proposition and that such propositions, rather than statements, should properly be understood as the bearers of logical form (see I.4.1.4.e). In any case, we recall that we turned our attention to statement logic in pursuit of our more general interest in logically valid inference or logical consequence. Our analysis of examples persuaded us that not all features of the statements contained in a valid inference are relevant to its validity. And so we will target those features that *are* relevant in an account of logical form. But the account of logical form to be developed in this chapter addresses only a particular class of logically valid inferences: the valid inferences of statement logic. The representation of their logical forms will require that we also develop a symbol system, with which forms will be captured in formulas.

1. The Symbol System of Statement Logic

1.1. *Truth-Functional Connectives*

Truth-functional connectives play a special role in statement logic. But we must take a closer look at several of them before considering this role.

Truth-functional connectives were well known to the philosophers of antiquity. Ludwig Wittgenstein (1889–1951) is credited with having invented the method of *truth tables,* a simple device for describing the behavior of such connectives. A truth table for a given statement provides an overview of all possible combinations of truth values for the constituent primitive statements and thus also reveals the (fully determinate) corresponding truth values for the entire statement. How might such a table look in practice?

a. Conjunction

We recall Example 1.11: "The apartment is nice and fairly expensive." If both of the constituent statements joined by the connective 'and' are true, then the statement as a whole is also true; if, on the other hand, one or the other constituent statement is false, or both, then the statement as a whole is false. The conjunction 'and', as it occurs in Example 1.11, is a truth-functional connective. Let us use 'A_1' as an abbreviation for 'The apartment is nice' and 'A_2' for 'The apartment is fairly expensive'. We will also use '$\wedge$' to take the place of the truth-functional 'and'; other symbols commonly used for this purpose include '&' and '•'. Our statement may now be rendered as '$A_1 \wedge A_2$'.

The dependence of the truth value of this statement on the truth values of the constituent statements A_1 and A_2 is thus displayed by the following table:

A_1	A_2	$A_1 \wedge A_2$
T	T	T
T	F	F
F	T	F
F	F	F

Each row represents one of the four possible combinations of truth values for A_1 and A_2, and in the far right column of each row we read the truth value of the entire statement. The truth-functional 'and' represented by '$\wedge$' in this table is known as the "conjunction" (not to be confused with the much broader grammatical notion by the same name). Correspondingly, the two statements joined by this connective are known as "conjuncts." The table itself is called the "truth table for conjunction."

It should be clear why the truth table device is applicable only to truth-functional connectives. With an intensional connective, it is not at all clear what should be put in the right-hand column, since by definition, the truth values of the constituent statements fail to determine the truth value of the compound statement. But for truth-functional connectives, the truth value of the compound statement is simply a function of the truth values of the constituent statements and is thus unequivocally determined by them.

In the above discussion I have been careful to refer to the "truth-functional 'and'," because the English word 'and' also has a common, non–truth-functional use. Consider the following example:

> **Example 2.1.** The doctor gave Bill some medicine, and Bill got better.

Here the word 'and' implies something like "and therefore". Example 2.1 should thus be understood as asserting that Bill got better *because* the doctor gave him some medicine. As we have seen, however (section I.4.3), 'because' is *not* a truth-functional connective. The 'and' in Example 2.1 is thus likewise nonextensional. Translating colloquial statements by means of symbolic connectives thus demands great care. Under no circumstances ought we to mechanically replace each and every 'and' with the truth-functional '∧'.

b. Disjunction

Our next truth-functional connective calls for a new example.

> **Example 2.2.** Bill is chatting with his mother or he is knitting.

This example is not entirely unambiguous. It is not clear whether this statement implies that Bill is either chatting with his mother or knitting, but not both, or whether it is consistent with the possibility that he *might* be doing both. The colloquial 'or' thus has two possible meanings: it can represent what is called the "exclusive 'or,'" as well as the "inclusive 'or.'" Both versions of the 'or' are truth-functional, as is easily seen. In logic, the inclusive 'or' is now called "disjunction" (perhaps a poor choice of words, since 'disjunction' originally referred to the *exclusive* 'or'). The two statements joined by this connective are called "disjuncts." The symbol for disjunction, '∨', is called the "vel," after the Latin word for the inclusive 'or'; its shape hearkens back to the initial 'v'. There is no conventional symbol for the exclusive 'or' in logic, though the abbreviation XOR is used in electrical engineering and computer science.

Let us take the 'or' in Example 2.2 as an inclusive 'or'. Using 'A_1' in place of "Bill is chatting with his mother," and 'A_2' in place of "Bill is knitting," along with '∨' in place of the inclusive 'or', we obtain the following truth table for disjunction:

A_1	A_2	$A_1 \vee A_2$
T	T	T
T	F	T
F	T	T
F	F	F

✱*Exercise 2.1.* Construct the truth table for the exclusive 'or', 'A_1 XOR A_2'.

c. Negation

Consider the following example:

> *Example 2.3.*   It is not the case that formal logic is a purely mathematical discipline.

This statement is precisely the opposite of "Formal logic is a purely mathematical discipline." The expression 'it is not the case that . . .' may be used to obtain from any statement a second statement whose truth value is the opposite of the first. 'It is not the case that . . .' is called "negation," and its symbol is '¬'. Accordingly, "It is not the case that A" can be written '¬A', which we read as "not A." Common alternatives to our symbol for negation include the tilde (as in '~*A*'), and the dash ('-*A*'). Now, negation is not used to *connect* statements; it is thus not, in this sense, strictly a truth-functional connective. But negation does allow for the truth-functional construction of one statement from another. It is thus frequently called a "unary connective," to contrast it with the "binary connectives," which join two statements to form a third. There is a truth table for negation, though it only contains two rows:

A	$\neg A$
T	F
F	T

Colloquial expressions of negation must be analyzed carefully. Negation is frequently expressed using only the word 'not', as when we negate the statement 'It is raining' by adding 'not', to form 'It is not raining', rather than the more cumbersome 'It is not the case that it is raining'. But depending on its placement, 'not' can do very different things, as in the following series of examples:

Example 2.4.   Quietly, a man left the bar.

Example 2.4a. Not quietly, a man left the bar.

Example 2.4b. Quietly, not a man left the bar.

Example 2.4c. Quietly, a man left not the bar.

In Examples 2.4a–c, the 'not' is used to negate something or other *inside* the original statement. Logical negation, by contrast, is global. The most straightforward way to write the logical negation of Example 2.4 appears to be

Example 2.4d. It is not the case that a man left the bar quietly.

✳*Exercise 2.2.* Using '*S*' as an abbreviation for 'The sun is shining' and '*H*' for 'The heavens are smiling', along with the logical symbols introduced above, rewrite the following statements:

1. The sun is shining, and the heavens are smiling.
2. The sun is shining, but the heavens are not smiling.
3. The heavens are smiling, and the sun is not shining.
4. The sun is not shining, and the heavens are not smiling.
5. The sun is not shining.

＊*Exercise 2.3.* In the following examples, identify the statements (or substatements) being negated.

1. $A_1 \vee (\neg A_2)$
2. $(\neg A_1) \vee A_2$
3. $\neg(A_1 \wedge A_2)$
4. $(\neg A_1) \wedge \neg(A_2 \wedge A_3)$
5. $\neg(A_1 \vee (A_2 \vee (\neg A_3)))$
6. $\neg(A_1 \wedge \neg((\neg A_2) \vee A_3))$

＊*Exercise 2.4.* English devices for forming compound statements are frequently ambiguous, especially when several occur together. Using the symbols introduced so far, along with '*B*' for 'Bill is crying', and '*F*' for 'Frank is crying', rewrite the following sentences:

1. Bill and Frank are both crying.
2. Bill is crying, but not Frank.
3. Neither Frank nor Bill is crying.
4. Both Bill and Frank are crying.
5. It is not Bill who is crying, but Frank.
6. It is not the case that Bill is crying and not Frank.
7. Bill and Frank are not both crying.
8. It is not the case that both Bill and Frank are crying.

＊*Exercise 2.5.* Rewrite the statement 'A_1 XOR A_2' using connectives $\wedge$, $\vee$, and $\neg$.

d. Conditional

We begin our discussion of the next extensional connective with the following example:

> **Example 2.5.**   If I have mastered logic by the time I finish this book, then I will give the book away.

'If . . . then' is yet another expression with which we may join two statements together to form a compound. Now we must ask whether it is truthfunctional, which means inquiring whether the truth value of a compound statement formed by means of this expression is entirely determined by the truth values of the two constituent statements. Let us abbreviate "I have mastered logic by the time I finish this book" as 'A_1', and "I will give this book away" as 'A_2'. Example 2.5 thus becomes 'If A_1, then A_2'. Now let us assume that you *will* have mastered logic by the time you finish this book and that you *will* give it away; we assume that both A_1 and A_2 are true. To all appearances, the truth of both constituent statements is enough to make the compound statement 'If A_1, then A_2' true. But now let us assume that by the time you have finished this book you have mastered logic (A_1 is true), but that you decide to lock it in your safe to prevent anyone from taking it from you (A_2 is false). Now it appears that the truth of A_1 together with the falsehood of A_2 is enough to make the compound statement false. So far, 'If . . . then' appears to be a truth-functional connective.

But what are we to say about the unfortunate and, needless to say, unlikely circumstance in which you have failed to master logic by the time you finish this book (A_1 is false)? Can the truth value of the compound statement be established, whether you decide to keep the book (A_2 is false) or offer it to the first taker (A_2 is true)? It appears the answer is "no," for if the condition "I have mastered logic by the time I finish this book" is *not* met, then the statement in Example 2.5 commits you to nothing. 'If . . . then' is thus not a truth-functional connective, for in those cases in which A_1 is false, the truth value of the compound statement is undetermined.

This preliminary result may be summarized in the following table:

A_1	A_2	If A_1, then A_2
T	T	T
T	F	F
F	T	undetermined
F	F	undetermined

At first blush, it appears that 'if . . . then' behaves like a truth-functional connective in those cases in which A_1 is true. But that is not right, either. Consider the case in which you have successfully mastered logic by the time you finish this book and subsequently give it away. The relation between your logic mastery and your generosity with books seems suspiciously substantial; it has the air of explanation: "*Because* I have mastered logic by the time I finished this book, I am giving it away." But, once again, we have already established that the connective 'because' is intensional (See I.4.3). This intensional component of the 'if . . . then' is most evident when we use it to form a compound statement out of two true statements whose contents are otherwise unrelated. Consider,

> *Example 2.6.* If freight trains are slower than passenger trains, then panthers are swifter than dachshunds.

But surely this statement is false, as you, dear reader, will have spotted immediately, for in order to be true, a statement of the form 'If A_1, then A_2' demands that there be some sort of substantive connection between the two constituent statements. No such connection is apparent in Example 2.6. Our provisional table for 'If . . . then' must thus be revised, for the truth values for A_1 and A_2 in the first row are compatible with *either* truth value for the compound statement.

A_1	A_2	If A_1, then A_2
T	T	T or F
T	F	F
F	T	undetermined
F	F	undetermined

Nonetheless, there remains a truth-functional *component* to 'if . . . then', a component that emerges on the second row. Anyone who asserts 'If A_1 then A_1' would surely want to deny that A_1 was true and A_2 simultaneously false, for the claim is simply that if condition A_1 is met, A_2 also obtains. Whether there is a substantial connection between A_1 and A_2 is irrelevant at this point. And this denial of 'A_1 and not A_2' *can* be captured by means of truth-functional connectives, since it amounts to the insistence that '$A_1 \wedge \neg A_2$' is *false*. But introducing a further negation, this is the same as asserting that '$\neg(A_1 \wedge \neg A_2)$' is *true*. And so the statement '$\neg(A_1 \wedge \neg A_2)$' just isolates the extensional portion of the statement 'If A_1 then A_2'. Since we will have frequent call for statements of the form '$\neg(A_1 \wedge \neg A_2)$', we will introduce a special symbolic connective, '$\rightarrow$', and write '$\neg(A_1 \wedge \neg A_2)$' as '$A_1 \rightarrow A_2$'. This connective is called the "conditional" or sometimes the "material conditional" (or "material implication"). In a statement of the form $A_1 \rightarrow A_2$, we call A_1 the "antecedent" of the conditional, and A_2 its "consequent." Another symbol commonly used in place of the arrow is the horseshoe, '$\supset$'.

What about the truth table for $A_1 \rightarrow A_2$? Clearly it is not the same as the table for 'if . . . then', as the conditional is not identical with 'if . . . then'. But since $A_1 \rightarrow A_2$ says the same thing as $\neg(A_1 \wedge \neg A_2)$, we should consider how to construct a truth table for the latter.

* If A_1 and A_2 are both true, then $\neg A_2$ is false. Thus $A_1 \wedge \neg A_2$ is false, and so $\neg(A_1 \wedge \neg A_2)$ must be true.
* If A_1 is true and A_2 false, then $\neg A_2$ is true. Therefore $A_1 \wedge \neg A_2$ is also true, and so $\neg(A_1 \wedge \neg A_2)$ must be false.
* If A_1 is false, then regardless of the truth value of A_2, $A_1 \wedge \neg A_2$ must be false, making $\neg(A_1 \wedge \neg A_2)$ true.

By this reasoning, we obtain the following truth table:

A_1	A_2	$\neg(A_1 \wedge \neg A_2)$
T	T	T
T	F	F
F	T	T
F	F	T

Which in turn yields an identical table for the connective '$\rightarrow$':

A_1	A_2	$A_1 \rightarrow A_2$
T	T	T
T	F	F
F	T	T
F	F	T

This, then, is the truth table for the conditional. A quick comparison of this table with the table for 'if . . . then' shows that the two are far from equivalent. Consider:

Row 1: Conditionals with true antecedents and true consequents are always true, whereas the corresponding 'if . . . then' statements can be either true or false. For example, the following statement is true:

> *Example 2.6a.* Freight trains are slower than passenger trains $\rightarrow$ panthers are swifter than dachshunds.

However, the 'if . . . then' formulation in the original Example 2.6 is false.

Row 2: Conditionals are like 'if . . . then' statements in that a true antecedent and false consequent make both sorts of statement false. This was the basis for our construction of the conditional.

Rows 3–4: A conditional with a false antecedent is always true, regardless of the truth value of its consequent.

> *Example 2.7.* I am rich $\rightarrow$ I will give each and every reader of this book a set of solar panels.

Now, since I am not rich, the conditional is true, regardless of whether I fulfill my promise of solar panels. However, the following *colloquial* statement is neither true nor false:

> *Example 2.7a.* If I am rich, then I will give each and every reader of this book a set of solar panels.

Given the fact that I am not rich, the condition in the 'if' clause fails to obtain, preventing any meaningful test of my promise.

The following moral may be drawn: *in general,* the conditional fails to adequately capture the colloquial 'if . . . then' because it abstracts from the intensional component of the latter. Only those statements of the form 'If A_1 then A_2' that really do mean $\neg(A_1 \wedge \neg A_2)$ can be accurately rendered by means of our conditional. Later on, our construction of the conditional will turn out to be useful in explicating the notion of logically valid inference—but that will have to wait.

>✳*Exercise 2.6.* Using 'A' as an abbreviation for 'Adam is coming', and 'E' for 'Eve is coming', and ignoring any intensional implications, rewrite the following sentences:
>
>1. If Adam is coming, Eve is also coming.
>2. Adam is coming only if Eve is also coming.
>3. In the case in which Eve is coming, Adam is also coming.
>4. Adam is not coming without Eve.
>5. Adam is coming just in case Eve is coming.
>6. Only if Adam is coming will Eve come.
>7. If Adam is coming, then Eve is coming.
>8. Eve is not coming unless Adam is coming.
>9. Eve is coming if and only if Adam is coming.

e. Biconditional

Once again, we begin with an example.

> *Example 2.8.*   I will be satisfied if, and only if, you read this book with
> rapt devotion.

The expression 'just in case' is another way of expressing the same relation:

> *Example 2.8a.*   I will be satisfied just in case you read this book with rapt
> devotion.

'If and only if' and 'just in case' are clearly somehow stronger or narrower than the 'if . . . then' discussed in the previous section. Examples 2.8 and 2.8a assert more than just that I will be satisfied *if* you read this book with rapt devotion. Something is also implied about how I will feel if you *fail* to satisfy this condition; in that case I will *not* be satisfied. The 'if and only if' statement is true whenever either both constituent statements are true or both are false. It is false whenever one constituent statement is true and the other false. Now if, as before, we abstract from the well-known intensional components of such statements (Example 2.8 implies a *causal* or *explanatory* connection between the two conditions), we arrive at the truth-functional connective known as the *biconditional,* or *(material) equivalence,* for which we introduce the symbol '$\leftrightarrow$' (The symbol '$\equiv$' frequently plays this role, but we shall reserve it for another purpose; see II.2.5). The truth table for the biconditional is as follows:

A_1	A_2	$A_1 \leftrightarrow A_2$
T	T	T
T	F	F
F	T	F
F	F	T

✻*Exercise 2.7.* How many ways are there of extensionally combining two statements? How many ways are there of combining them intensionally?

﹡*Exercise 2.8.* Selecting appropriate abbreviations for atomic statements, and abstracting from all intensional factors, rewrite the following sentences:

1. When a burglary or fire has occurred, the insurance company pays for the damages.

2. Bill is going to the movie only if Ed is going to the movie and there is nothing good on TV, and if Bill does not go to the movie, then he will either do the dishes and water the plants or call his sweetheart.

3. If Frances does not come Sarah will be upset, and Frances will not come unless Alex comes, and if Alex comes Sarah will be upset.

4. If Mr. Miller is sick and Ms. Meyers is absent, then the contract will not be signed and the board will not meet nor set the dividend.

5. It is not true that the roads only ice up when it is both below freezing and either raining or foggy.

f. Concluding Remarks on the Connectives

We have now introduced the most important truth-functional connectives—most important in the sense that they are most needed for purposes of explicating logical consequence and related notions. One further remark is in order. In the literature one sometimes encounters the claim that the connectives are defined by their truth tables, in the sense that it is the tables that unequivocally fix their meanings. This claim is correct insofar as we understand the connectives in a highly specific mathematical sense, as functions that map pairs of statements (or single statements, in the case of negation), to the set of truth values, {T, F}. On the other hand, if we treat the connectives as tools for constructing statements, as operators with which we may form new compound statements on the basis of one or two constituent statements, then they are *not* defined by their truth tables. This can be shown in six easy steps (feel free to take notes!).

1. Step 1: We begin by comparing any arbitrary statement *A* with the statement 'It is true that *A*'; for example, 'The house is nice' with 'It is true that the house is nice'. The first of these two statements clearly asserts something about a particular house, namely that it is nice. But the second

statement is not about the house at all but rather about the *statement* 'The house is nice'. What *it* asserts is that the statement in question is true. Since the two statements are about different things, it follows that they are different statements. So, in general, statement A is distinct from the statement 'It is true that A'.

2. Step 2: Now compare the statement '$A_1 \wedge A_2$' with the statement '$A_1 \wedge$ it is true that A_2'. By step 1, these two statements are distinct, since they differ in the second conjunct.

3. Step 3: The statement '$A_1 \wedge$ it is true that A_2' can also be parsed as composed of the statement A_1, the connective ' . . . $\wedge$ it is true that . . .', and the statement A_2.

4. Step 4: By step 2, the statements '$A_1 \wedge A_2$' and '$A_1 \wedge$ it is true that A_2' are distinct. By step 3, we may trace the difference between them to the fact that they employ different connectives, '$\wedge$' and ' . . . $\wedge$ and it is true that . . .', respectively. It follows that these connectives must also be distinct.

5. Step 5: But the connective ' . . . $\wedge$ and it is true that . . .' has the same truth table as the conjunction '$\wedge$'. For as is easily seen, statements A_2 and 'it is true that A_2' will always have the same truth value.

6. Step 6: By step 4, the two connectives, '$\wedge$' and ' . . . $\wedge$ and it is true that . . . ,' are distinct, while by step 5 they have the same truth tables. It thus follows that there are two different connectives with the same truth tables. This proves that truth tables do not unequivocally determine the meanings of connectives and thus do not define them.

Of course, the crucial difference, set out in step 1, between A and 'It is true that A', is not terribly great, though there are contexts in which it becomes significant. Later on, however, this particular difference will turn out not to matter for purposes of formal logic. This argument will have to wait until section II.2.5.b.

1.2. Statement Form

a. Definition

As has been emphasized, our goal in introducing the notion of logical form is to precisely isolate those features of statements relevant to the validity of inferences. The specific concept of logical form to which we now turn is called "statement form," and it is geared toward a particular class of logically valid inferences. As to whether statement form, as defined below, does the job it is supposed to do, this question cannot be addressed until the relevant class of inferences has been properly introduced (see II.2.4). For now, our definition of statement form is as follows:

> **Definition 2.1.** A statement form (SF) of a statement is obtained by abstracting away the meanings of its truth-functionally combined constituent statements or the meaning of the whole statement. However, sameness or difference of those constituent statements is part of the respective statement form.

By this definition, an SF of a statement is obtained by abstracting away the meanings of truth-functionally connected constituent statements or the meaning of the statement itself. There is one limiting condition in the definition: abstraction must not be taken so far as to obscure the identities—sameness or difference—of constituent statements; these are part of the SF. Implicit in the abstraction procedure is the following. The *connectives* by means of which those constituent statements are linked, whose meanings are abstracted away, belong to the SF.

Let us bring this discussion back down to earth by returning to a familiar case, Example 1.11: "The apartment is nice and fairly expensive." To obtain an SF of this statement, our definition requires that we abstract away the meanings of extensionally combined constituent statements. In this instance, we must thus forget about the niceness of the apartment and its price. We instead think of the statement merely as a truth-functional compound of two constituent statements, linked together by means of conjunction. What we must not abstract away, however, is the fact these two constituent statements are different from one another.

Thinking of statements in this way yields SFs that exist only as objects of thought. But with the help of symbols, we are now able to represent such SFs fairly easily. A representation of an SF is composed of the familiar symbols for truth-functional connectives, along with lowercase letters, usually 'p', 'q', 'r', in place of the constituent primitive statements whose meanings have been abstracted away. These are called "(schematic) sentential letters." The equally common name of "statement variable" is somewhat misleading, as nothing varies! Returning to Example 1.11, after abstracting away the first conjunct ("The apartment is nice"), we write down a sentential letter, such as 'p', to fill the resulting gap. Since sentential letters fill the gaps that result from the abstraction of statements, they take the places of statements and are therefore also called "placeholders." After the first such placeholder comes the conjunction, which remains, and then a second gap in place of the second conjunct. But since the second conjunct ("The apartment is fairly expensive") is different from the first, the gap it leaves must, in accordance with the limiting condition of Definition 2.1, be filled by a different placeholder—for example, 'q'. Thus, an SF that was gained by process of abstraction, resulting in an object of thought, is now easily represented as $p \wedge q$.

b. Further Remarks on the Notion of Statement Form

1. It is worth noting the difference between the SF $p \wedge q$ and the superficially similar $A_1 \wedge A_2$. As introduced, $A_1 \wedge A_2$ is an *abbreviation;* as used above, it is an abbreviation for "The apartment is nice and [the apartment is] fairly expensive." An abbreviation replaces expressions with other, shorter expressions without changing the meaning being expressed. For example, the meaning of the abbreviation 'ltd.' is supposed to be the same as that of the full expression, 'limited liability association'. By contrast, '$p \wedge q$' is meant to represent the end product of a particular abstraction process, one in which almost the entire meaning of the original statement is stripped away, leaving only the SF, in which nothing whatsoever is said

about apartments. We should not allow ourselves to be deceived by the typographic similarity between '$A_1 \wedge A_2$' and '$p \wedge q$'.

2. One immediate consequence of the aforementioned difference between '$A_1 \wedge A_2$' and '$p \wedge q$' is that while the former has a truth value (it is, after all, a statement), the latter does not. In $p \wedge q$ we have abstracted away the meanings of the constituent statements, and the meaningfulness of a sentence is a necessary condition for its truth or falsehood. In general, then, SFs have no truth values; they are not statements.

3. The distinctions introduced in section I.4 were specifically geared toward the notion of SF we have now established. In that section we moved from sentences, to statements, to compound statements, and finally to extensional connectives. The extensional connectives are the primary subject matter of statement logic, in the sense that the valid inferences of statement logic turn on the properties of these connectives. We will return to this topic later.

4. In the representation of the SF of a statement we must always remember to use the same sentential letters for the same constituent statements and to use different sentential letters for different constituent statements. As formalized in the limiting condition of Definition 2.1, the sameness and difference of extensionally joined primitive statements belong to logical form, not content. As to why this is the case, this too will have to wait for our treatment of the notion of valid inference proper to statement logic.

In most instances it is easy to decide whether two primitive statements are the same or different. But there are problematic cases, and dealing with them would be more straightforward if we had an explicit criterion for the sameness and difference of statements. However, any such criterion would have to depend on how we answered the question of what a statement actually *is* (compare section I.4.1). If, for example, we understand a statement as a particular physical inscription or pattern of sound waves, then *all* statements are different. 'It is raining' would be different from 'It is raining', since the two inscriptions on your page are composed of different ink particles. On the other hand, if statements are individuated typographically, then the two instances of 'It is raining' are the same, but both are different from 'IT IS RAINING' and '*It is raining*'. Of course, if we ignore such typographic differences, then these, too, are instances of the same statement. But what about 'Está lloviendo' and 'Es regnet' (the esteemed reader is invited to guess at the meanings of these statements)? These examples should suffice to show that any criterion for the sameness and difference of statements would depend on what we mean by "statement."

A great deal of formal logic depends on the distinction between same and different statements. Without posing any obstacles to purely formal manipulations, the distinction itself remains largely obscure. But if our goal is an understanding of logic that transcends the merely technical, we must also probe the very presuppositions on which the technical apparatus rests, and in doing so we find ourselves searching for a criterion for the sameness and difference of statements, which in turn leads us back to the question of what statements are in the first place. Here, as in many other contexts, we find philosophical problems emerging out of a comparatively mundane practice, problems that easily go unnoticed so long as the practice itself continues to work. Part of the task of philosophy is to detect and reveal such problems, and thus to anticipate difficulties even when the practice in question remains, for the moment, trouble free. Plainly, from the perspective of a well-oiled practice, such philosophizing might seem to be a pointless undertaking. But even the most theory-adverse of all practitioners find themselves turning more theoretical once their treasured practice becomes mired in difficulty.

5. When a given statement contains several connectives, we must, before we can turn to its SFs, first set *parentheses,* so as to make it clear which constituent statements are joined by which connectives. Consider the following:

> *Example 2.9.*   Patricia went to the bookstore and bought a logic book or stole a novel.

This sentence contains two connectives, 'and' and 'or'. Depending on context, we might understand this statement in two different ways. The use of parentheses provides an inelegant but effective way of distinguishing them:

> *Example 2.9a.* Patricia went to the bookstore and (bought a logic book or
> stole a novel).

This first reading definitely asserts that Patricia went to the bookstore; what remains in question is whether what she did there is praise- or blameworthy.

> *Example 2.9b.* (Patricia went to the bookstore and bought a logic book) or
> stole a novel.

By contrast with Example 2.9a, this second reading does not tell us for certain whether Patricia ever even went to the bookstore. She might have stolen a novel from her grandmother!

Before any attempt can be made to derive a logical form from Example 2.9, we must first decide what the statement means to assert—that is, where the parentheses should be placed. The reason is that 2.9a and 2.9b differ significantly with regard to what they allow us to infer. From 2.9a we may validly infer that Patricia went to the bookstore—but this does not follow from 2.9b. Why does it matter that 2.9a and 2.9b have different logical consequences? Logic is the study of valid inference, among other things, and the validity of inferences can only be studied if it is sufficiently clear *from which* statements we are inferring. It is valid to infer from 2.9a that Patricia went to the bookstore—but to draw this inference from 2.9b would be invalid.

We will thus permit our representations of SFs to contain parentheses; indeed, they *must* contain parentheses whenever the forms in question involve more than one connective. Reading the 'and' in 2.9a as truth-functional and the 'or' as inclusive, a plausible logical form for this example would be $p \wedge (q \vee r)$, while 2.9b becomes $(p \wedge q) \vee r$.

6. By now it should be clear why Definition 2.1 begins with the indefinite article 'A' in defining "A statement form of a statement": a given statement can have *several different* SFs. For Example 2.9a, we have already considered the logical form $p \wedge (q \vee r)$. But if we allow our abstraction to be a bit more coarse-grained, distinguishing only between the trip to the bookstore and what took place there, *whatever that might have been,* then another SF for 2.9a would be $p \wedge s$. Definition 2.1 does not prohibit us from treating any one of the extensionally joined constituent statements as a unit, even if this unit is itself a truth-functional compound. An even coarser SF is obtained by abstracting from the entire meaning of the statement, yielding simply t. Thus the single statement "Patricia went to the bookstore and (bought a logic book or stole a novel)" yields three different SFs: $p \wedge (q \vee r)$, $p \wedge s$, and t. Of course, a statement that is not truth-functionally composed, an atomic statement, has only one SF.

✳Exercise 2.9. Let *A, B,* and *C* be statements. Give all possible SFs for the statement $((\neg A) \leftrightarrow B) \rightarrow \neg((\neg B) \wedge C)$.

7. We are now ready for the definitions of three of statement logic's most useful concepts:

Definition 2.2. The representation of an SF by means of sentential letters, along with connectives and parentheses (if needed), is called a "formula of statement logic" or "SL formula."

As an example of an SL formula, consider the following:

Example 2.10. $((p \wedge r) \vee (q \wedge r)) \rightarrow (p \leftrightarrow (\neg r))$

A given SL formula represents or denotes a particular SF, an object of thought, produced by a particular way of abstracting from a given statement.

Definition 2.3. The move from a statement to one of its SFs, and from the SF to a corresponding SL formula, is called the "SL formalization" of the statement.

The SL formalization of a statement thus consists in two steps: one of abstraction, in arriving at the SF, and one of representation, in rendering the SF as an SL formula.

> *Definition 2.4.* The connective between the two largest subformulas of an SL formula is called the "main connective" of the formula. If the SL formula consists in a negation followed by a single subformula enclosed in parentheses, this negation is the main connective.

SL formulas are also named after their main connectives. For example, $p \wedge (q \vee r)$ is called a "conjunction," $(p \wedge q) \rightarrow (r \vee s)$ is called a "conditional" (or "implication"), and $\neg (p \wedge q)$ is called a "negation." In a well-formed formula that contains connectives there is never any doubt as to which is the main connective.

> *✴Exercise 2.10.* Classify each of the following formulas by type (conjunction, disjunction, etc.).
>
> 1. $(p \wedge q) \vee (p \rightarrow s)$
> 2. $p \leftrightarrow (q \leftrightarrow s)$
> 3. $((p \rightarrow q) \wedge r) \rightarrow q$
> 4. $(\neg (p \vee r)) \vee (\neg q)$
> 5. $(\neg (p \rightarrow r)) \rightarrow (\neg (p \vee r))$
> 6. $\neg ((p \rightarrow r) \rightarrow s)$
> 7. $q \vee (\neg (p \vee r))$

8. Longer SL formulas frequently contain numerous pairs of parentheses. For our convenience in reading and writing such formulas, logicians observe a set of *parenthesis conventions*. Similar conventions are familiar from arithmetic and algebra. For example, '$3 + 2 \times 5$' means $3 + (2 \times 5)$, and *not* $(3 + 2) \times 5$; in a sense, we understand there to be invisible parentheses around 2×5, in accordance with the rule "times before plus." Or, in other words, multiplication *takes precedence over* addition. In $3 + 2 \times 5$, the $\times$ takes precedence over the $+$, in that the former operation must be

carried out first. An analogous precedence order, or order of operations, holds for our logical connectives. Many authors observe the following order of operations: $\neg$, $\wedge$, $\vee$, $\rightarrow$, and $\leftrightarrow$. By this ordering, we may write '$p \rightarrow q \leftrightarrow r$' instead of '$(p \rightarrow q) \leftrightarrow r$', or '$\neg p \vee q$' in place of '$(\neg p) \vee q$'. Still observing the same ordering, we could also write '$p \wedge q \vee r$' in place of '$(p \wedge q) \vee r$'. But caution is called for. Some authors reverse the precedence ordering of conjunction and disjunction, and a great many treat all binary connectives as of equal precedence, though of lower precedence than negation. I will treat conjunction and disjunction as of equal precedence and always enclose them in parentheses. Otherwise, I will observe the order of operations given above.

**Exercise 2.11.* Rewrite the following formulas in accordance with the order of operations given above.

    1. $(p \wedge q) \rightarrow (q \rightarrow r)$
    2. $(p \wedge q) \rightarrow (q \vee r)$
    3. $(p \wedge q) \leftrightarrow (q \rightarrow r)$
    4. $(p \wedge q) \vee (q \rightarrow r)$
    5. $(\neg(p \vee q)) \rightarrow (p \wedge q)$

9. The formalization of statements is very closely analogous to the move from numerical equations to algebraic formulas. For example, '$2 + 3 = 3 + 2$' has the algebraic form $a + b = b + a$. Just as sentential letters serve as placeholders for statements, so letters a and b serve as placeholders for whole or real numbers.

1.3. The Interpretation of SL Formulas

Once statements have been abstracted to form SFs, the latter are no longer true or false (compare section II.1.2.b.2). For reasons which will become more clear later on, we now ask whether this abstraction process is reversible and how.

a. Intensional Interpretation

How might we reverse the abstraction process leading from a statement to an SF? It turns out to be quite easy, provided we have kept a record of the original meanings of the constituent statements, now abstracted away. As we recall, we arrived at SL formula $p \land (q \lor r)$ for Example 2.9a. Now insert the statement "Patricia went to the bookstore" in place of 'p', "Patricia bought a logic book" in place of 'q', and "Patricia stole a novel" in place of 'r'. The substitution goes through smoothly precisely because the sentential letters have been serving as placeholders for statements. If in the interim we have forgotten which constituent statements were abstracted away, we might instead use $p \land (q \lor r)$ to generate another statement by substituting arbitrary statements in place of 'p', 'q', and 'r'. The result will be a statement whose truth value will naturally depend on the truth values of the constituent statements we have chosen. The process thus described has a name:

> **Definition 2.5.** An intensional interpretation of an SL formula is produced by assigning statements to the sentential letters of the formula. The same statements must always be assigned to the same sentential letters.

Intensional interpretation involves the complete reversal of the process of abstraction from statement to SF. The word 'interpretation', as it occurs here and elsewhere in logical parlance, is somewhat misleading. Like 'statement' (compare section I.4.1.3), it is a technical term whose meaning diverges significantly from the corresponding colloquial expression or from concepts of interpretation employed in the other fields of scholarship. In colloquial speech, 'interpretation' refers to the process of extracting something from whatever is being interpreted, where this something is understood as really already *contained* in it: its meaning. Here, by contrast, an interpretation is an *assignment,* for sentential letters do not contain any meanings. The notion of interpretation described in Definition 2.5 is called "intensional" because it involves the ascription of statement meanings, or *intensions,* to sentential letters. Intensional interpretation is completely straightforward, so let us move on.

b. Extensional Interpretation

Suppose we are interested in reversing the abstraction to an SL formula in such a way as to determine how different interpretations assign potentially differing truth values to the formula (this kind of reversal will turn out to be very interesting indeed). Consider $p \wedge q$. If we are interested in discovering which interpretations make this formula true, there is no need to try out all possible assignments of statements to p and q. It is enough to examine the truth table for conjunction, which tells us that formula $p \wedge q$ is assigned the value T just in case the statements assigned to both p and q are true, irrespective of what those statements actually mean. For present purposes it thus suffices to assign a truth value to each sentential letter in the formula being interpreted, thus assigning a truth value to the formula itself. Ascribing meaning to the sentential letters is unnecessary. When we assign value T to both p and q, we find that value T has likewise been assigned to the formula $p \wedge q$. By contrast, when T is assigned to p and F assigned to q, the formula has truth value F. This procedure also has a name.

> **Definition 2.6.** An extensional interpretation (or evaluation) of an SL formula consists in an assignment of truth values to the sentential letters of the formula, where the same truth values are always assigned to the same sentential letters.

Unlike intensional interpretation, extensional interpretation involves only *partial* reversal of the process of abstraction from statement to SF. This minimal assignment of truth values to sentential letters is enough to restore the property of veridicality (of being true or false), lost in the course of abstraction. Extensional interpretation is clearly geared toward extensional connectives and the associated SFs. For intensional compounds, such as '*p* because *q*' extensional interpretation fails to restore veridicality. Taken together, the notions of an extensional connective, statement form, and extensional interpretation will play a crucial role in our explication of valid inference. From now on I will often use "interpretation" to mean extensional interpretation, since it is this kind of interpretation with which the following discussion is primarily concerned.

c. *Truth Analysis*

I begin with a definition:

> **Definition 2.7.** The computation of the truth value of an extensionally interpreted SL formula is called a "truth analysis."

As our first example, consider the formula $p \land (q \lor r)$. First, we arbitrarily assign value *T* to sentential letters *p* and *q*, and value *F* to *r*. Next we write out the formula, placing the appropriate truth values under each sentential letter:

$$p \land (q \lor r)$$
$$\text{T} \quad \text{T} \quad \text{F}$$

As a next step, we write the truth values associated with those connectives that join individual sentential letters:

$$p \land (q \lor r)$$
$$\text{T} \quad \text{T} \quad \text{F}$$
$$\text{T}$$

Taking our procedure one step further, we now assign truth values wherever possible. In the present example, this takes us to the end, allowing us to write a truth value under the main connective of our formula:

$$p \land (q \lor r)$$
$$\text{T} \quad \text{T} \quad \text{F}$$
$$\text{T}$$
$$\text{T}$$

On the given interpretation, the truth value assigned to our SL formula is thus T.

As a further practice exercise, let us attempt Example 2.10, assigning T to p and q and F to r. We first write T under every instance of p and q, and F under every instance of r. The full evaluation takes four steps, yielding:

$$((p \wedge r) \vee (q \wedge r)) \to (p \leftrightarrow \neg r)$$

T	F	T	F		T	F	first step
	F		F			T	second step
		F			T		third step
			T				fourth and final step

Later on, we will make frequent use of a method for performing the truth analysis of a formula under all possible extensional interpretations. It is easily explained. First we modify our earlier procedure, and instead of writing out the truth values for each step on a separate line, we condense them all on one. Each interpretation thus results in a single row of truth values beneath the formula. Next we must ensure that each row represents a unique combination of assignments of truth values to the sentential letters and that all such combinations are captured. An elementary combinatorial analysis tells us there must be 2^n different combinations, where n is the number of different sentential letters in the formula in question. As an illustration of our procedure, consider the formula $p \wedge (q \to r)$. To be sure we have covered every possible interpretation, we must assign every possible combination of truth values to the three sentential letters, where there are $2^3 = 8$ such combinations. In the column under the first sentential letter, we write four Ts, followed by four Fs. Under the next sentential letter, we write two Ts, two Fs, two Ts, then finally two more Fs. For the final sentential letter, we alternate Ts and Fs until we reach the eighth row. Should a given sentential letter occur more than once in a formula, the column under its first occurrence is duplicated for all subsequent occurrences. For our present example, the procedure yields:

$$p \wedge (q \to r)$$

T	T	T
T	T	F
T	F	T
T	F	F
F	T	T
F	T	F
F	F	T
F	F	F

Now we carry out a truth analysis for each of the eight interpretations, writing out the results on the corresponding line:

$$p \wedge (q \to r)$$

T **T**	T	T	T
T **F**	T	F	F
T **F**	F	T	T
T **T**	F	T	F
F **F**	T	T	T
F **F**	T	F	F
F **F**	F	T	T
F **F**	F	T	F

There is a name for such charts, too:

Definition 2.8. The truth table of a given formula is a chart depicting the truth analysis of the formula under all interpretations. The column under the main connective of the formula is called the "main column."

The main column, here printed in boldface, is what really interests us, for it tells us how the formula itself behaves under all the various interpretations. We will need to know how to construct such truth tables—how to perform the analysis of all possible extensional interpretations of a given formula—in order to explicate the notion of valid inference. For now, though, they remain an amusing game (at least for some).

✳*Exercise 2.12.* Construct truth tables for the following formulas.

1. $p \leftrightarrow \neg\neg p$
2. $p \leftrightarrow p \wedge p$
3. $p \leftrightarrow p \vee p$
4. $p \wedge q \leftrightarrow q \vee p$
5. $p \vee q \leftrightarrow q \vee p$
6. $(p \wedge q) \wedge r \leftrightarrow p \wedge (q \wedge r)$
7. $(p \vee q) \vee r \leftrightarrow p \vee (q \vee r)$
8. $(p \rightarrow q) \rightarrow r \leftrightarrow p \rightarrow (q \rightarrow r)$
9. $(p \rightarrow q) \wedge (q \rightarrow p)$
10. $p \vee \neg p$
11. $p \wedge \neg p$

1.4. Summary

This concludes our introduction to the symbol system of statement logic. It has consisted of four main steps. We began by identifying the extensional connectives. Next we learned how to abstract statements so as to arrive at statement forms, after which we laid out the symbol system for statement logic. Finally, we studied the partial reversal of our abstraction process by means of extensional interpretations.

2. The Metalogic of Statement Logic

2.1. Object-Level and Metalevel

The distinction between logic and metalogic advertised in the header of this section is in fact a special case of a more general distinction between object-level and metalevel. Put in general and somewhat simplified terms, the metalevel somehow takes the object-level as *its* object. One very common version of the distinction is applied to language, allowing us to separate an object-language from a (corresponding) metalanguage. The metalanguage is used to talk about the object-language; the latter is the *object* of the former. Consider, for example, a textbook, written in English, on the

Spanish language. Such a book contains both English and Spanish sentences. The sentences of the Spanish practice texts, in which we are told, say, about what José does on his shopping trip, are object-language sentences. By contrast, the English sentences, which explain, for example, how to form the Spanish subjunctive, are metalanguage sentences whose object is the Spanish language. The distinction between object-language and metalanguage is also commonly articulated in terms of ordered levels of language:

The downward arrow ('↓') in this chart stands for the relation of linguistic reference in which expressions in higher-level languages refer to items at lower levels.

More than one level may be implemented within one and the same language, and consequently determining to which level a given expression belongs is not always as easy as in the example of the Spanish textbook written in English. Consider the following:

Example 2.11. Vienna is a city.

This example is plainly an ordinary, object-language sentence of English. Its object is Vienna, which *is* a city, and thus not a piece of language ("object" should here be understood in a broad sense as simply that of which we are speaking). On the other hand, the object in

Example 2.12. 'Vienna' is a name.

is not the city itself, but rather the name of the city. This sentence thus belongs to a metalanguage. The use of single quotation marks around 'Vienna' is meant to show that we are not talking about a thing, in this case a city, but rather about a word, in this case the *name* of the city. We will enclose object-language expressions in single quotation marks whenever it becomes important to acknowledge that we are talking on the metalanguage level. Even colloquial speech provides examples—though they are a bit forced—of instances in which the use of quotation marks would help eliminate ambiguity:

Example 2.13. John is monosyllabic.

At first blush, this appears to be an object-language sentence about John. But what if the John in question is very talkative? Is the speaker of this sentence necessarily saying something false? This could still be a true metalanguage sentence, if we placed quotation marks around the name 'John'. Then the speaker would be asserting, truthfully, that the name 'John' has only one syllable.

Before we come to the meat of our distinction between logic and metalogic, four further remarks on the levels of language are in order.

1. The medieval logicians distinguished different levels of language, as in William of Ockham's (1285?–1349) Doctrine of Supposition, but their work later fell into obscurity. The distinction was reintroduced in twentieth-century formal logic.

2. In the twentieth century, the distinction was motivated by the desire to avoid certain paradoxes that had arisen in the foundations of mathematics and logic. As an example of such a paradox, consider "This sentence is false." Try to see what makes this sentence paradoxical!

3. The practice of referring to the different levels of language as languages in their own right—for example, as object-language and metalanguage—can lead to confusion. When the English language is used at both the object-level and the metalevel, this does not cause it to disintegrate into two different languages. It is rather a matter of there being one language in which we may talk about different sorts of things: about nonlinguistic objects or about expressions in the language itself. We may thus assign various English sentences to one or another level of language (though

as we have seen, this can sometimes prove difficult), without there having to be two genuinely different languages. Besides the textbook example given above, the analysis of certain artificial languages provides the only context in which object-language and metalanguage are literally different languages. Some pairs of artificial languages are deliberately so constructed so as to make one suitable for talking only about nonlinguistic objects, while the other may also be used for talking about expressions in the first, the designated object-language.

4. The distinction between linguistic object- and metalevels is iterative, in the sense that we may also introduce a meta-metalevel. We reach this meta-metalevel once we begin talking about the metalevel; and once we begin talking about the meta-metalevel, we have reached the meta-meta-metalevel, and so on. In fact, any introduction to logic tacitly involves numerous assertions at levels of language higher than the first metalevel.

Our goal for the next several sections is to explicate the statement logic conception of logically valid inference (or logical consequence), along with related notions. Valid inference is a particular relation between statements (premises and conclusion). This notion of valid inference, or logical consequence, thus belongs to the metalevel, for to say that a given inference is valid is to say something about certain statements. While we will have a great deal to say about valid inference, there are many properties of statements and relations among them in which we are not especially interested. We are concerned only with those that obtain in virtue of the logical forms of statements, as we shall discover. For present purposes, then, it will suffice to develop that part of metalanguage known as "metalogic," or, more specifically, the "metalogic of statement logic." In what follows, we will analyze particular metalogical concepts using the same procedure employed in section II.1: for each concept, we will examine an example with a view toward the specific characteristics relevant to the precise explication of our concept. We will not begin with the notion of valid inference but rather with that of logical truth. This will allow us to introduce the former by way of the latter.

2.2. Logical Truth
a. Definition

As a first example, we begin with an old wives' tale. It will lead us to the heart of the matter, as old wives' tales so often do.

> *Example 2.14.* If the rooster crows on the manure pile, either the weather will change or it will stay as it is.

Let us consider the rather peculiar features of this folk aphorism.

1. The statement is undoubtedly true, but in a rather strange way. If the rooster does crow on the manure pile, then the weather may do as it pleases—change or stay as it is—and the statement is still true. On the other hand, if the rooster does not crow, or does not crow on the manure pile, the statement is not false, either. In a certain sense, the statement is empty, for it is always true no matter what happens. It thus contains no information about any events that might occur or fail to occur. But this emptiness in no way changes the fact that the statement is true.

2. In order to assess the truth of this statement, we need know nothing about the crowing behavior of roosters (or, in general, about bird ethology), about manure piles (agronomy), or about meteorology, nor need we know anything about the connections among these disciplines. It is enough to understand the statement and in the process to recognize that it is true under all circumstances. Convincing ourselves of its truth requires absolutely no knowledge of the things the statement purports to be about. Indeed, from a certain perspective, it does not matter *what* the statement is about. This is further confirmed by the following feature.

3. We may replace the constituent statements of Example 2.14 with any statements we like without affecting in the slightest the truth of the statement as a whole. Of course performing this replacement would change the statement, but that is not what matters here; what matters is that the peculiar truth of the statement is unaffected by the replacement of its constituent statements.

Example 2.15. If the snake eats the rabbit, then either the weather will change or it will stay as it is.

Example 2.16. If the rooster crows on the manure pile, then either the political climate will change or it will stay as it is.

4. The peculiar truth of Example 2.14 has to do rather with the structure of the statement: *If* something happens, *then either* something else occurs *or not*. It makes no difference what the two events are.

Now, what I have just called the "structure of the statement" looks a lot like a candidate logical form for Example 2.14. So let us derive an SF for this statement. We start by introducing 'A_1' as an abbreviation for 'The rooster crows on the manure pile', and 'A_2' for 'The weather will change.' Clearly, 'The weather will stay as it is' can be abbreviated as '$\neg A_2$'. We have now arrived at 'If A_1, then either A_2 or $\neg A_2$' as an abbreviation for Example 2.14. In order to proceed to an SF, we must first decide how to deal with the connective 'if . . . then'. Is this an extensional connective? Since there really is no causal connection between rooster-crowing and the weather, we might try treating the 'if . . . then' as purely extensional, reducing it to the conditional. This does change the statement, but only in the following respect: if the 'if' clause of Example 2.14 is false—that is, the rooster does not crow on the manure pile—then the statement as a whole will not be *false,* but its truth value will be undetermined. Replacing the 'if . . . then' by the conditional fixes the truth value for this case, making the statement as a whole true. With this modification, Example 2.14 becomes:

Example 2.17. $A_1 \rightarrow (A_2 \vee \neg A_2)$

Again, Example 2.17 constitutes a modification of 2.14, but for our purposes the departure is insignificant. We are now one step away from an obvious SF. All we have to do is abstract away from the meanings of A_1 and A_2, replacing them with sentential letters. What is left is $p \rightarrow (q \vee \neg q)$. The truth table for this formula is as follows:

p	$\rightarrow$	$(q$	$\vee$	$\neg$	$q)$
T	**T**	T	T	F	T
T	**T**	F	T	T	F
F	**T**	T	T	F	T
F	**T**	F	T	T	F

As the main column makes clear, this formula is true under *all* extensional interpretations. Since it is true under all extensional interpretations, it is also true under all *intensional* interpretations, for the meanings of the constituent statements do not affect the truth value of the statement as a whole, precisely because the statement is a truth-functional compound. In other words, *any* statement that has the above formula as one of its SFs *must* be true.

The basis for the somewhat peculiar truth of our original example is now clear. Its truth derives exclusively from one of the statement's SFs and is independent of both the meanings and truth values of its constituent statements, and thus it is independent of any concrete interpretation of the SL formula representing the SF in question. The four features of Example 2.14 cited above have now been explained. The peculiar kind of truth now coming into view is called "logical truth," and we have been dealing with a specific variety of it, namely "statement-logical truth," also known as "tautology." This notion is captured in the following definition:

Definition 2.9

1. An SF or SL formula is called a "(statement-)logical truth" or "(statement-)logically true" or a "tautology" or "tautologous," just in case it is true under all extensional interpretations.

2. A statement is called a "(statement-)logical truth" or "(statement-)logically true" or a "tautology" or "tautologous," just in case (at least) one of its SFs is a tautology.

We will use '⊨' as a symbol for logical truth. '(Statement or formula) A is logically true' may thus be rewritten as '⊨A'. Definition 2.9 suggests three further remarks.

1. The definition proceeds in two steps. The notion of tautology is first defined for SFs and SL formulas, and then *this* definition is used to define tautology for statements. In order to determine whether a given statement is tautologous, one must first examine its SFs with a view toward *their* logical truth.

2. Example 2.14, with which we began, also has *nontautologous* SFs. For example, '*p*→*r*' and '*s*' are both legitimate SFs for this statement, but clearly neither is a tautology. In other words, even with a tautologous statement, it is possible to abstract away so much that the very characteristics that make it a tautology also disappear. The second part of our definition thus requires only that a tautologous statement have "(at least) one" tautologous SF. It does *not* demand that *the* SF of the statement be tautologous (which would imply, falsely, that the statement has only one), nor does it insist that *all* SFs be tautologies.

3. With Definition 2.9 in place, the motive behind the particular way in which the concept of statement form was introduced, in Definition 2.1, should now be clear. It should also be clear why we needed the notion of extensional interpretation. Statement form was needed in order to define statement-logical truth. For the "mechanism" of a tautology is purely a matter of connectives, together with the sameness and difference of constituent statements, while the contents of those constituent statements are irrelevant. The fact that it is the connectives and the identities of constituent statements that play the decisive role is further reinforced by consideration of the very prototype of all tautologies, the statement $A \lor \neg A$. If we were to delete the negation, substitute conjunction for disjunction, or replace the second '*A*' with a '*B*', the statement would forfeit its tautologous status.

✳*Exercise 2.13.* Construct truth tables for the following formulas.

1. $p \to p \lor q$
2. $p \land q \to p$
3. $p \land (q \lor r) \leftrightarrow (p \land q) \lor (p \land r)$

4. $p \lor (q \land r) \leftrightarrow (p \lor q) \land (p \lor r)$
5. $\neg(p \land q) \leftrightarrow \neg p \lor \neg q$
6. $\neg(p \lor q) \leftrightarrow \neg p \land \neg q$
7. $p \rightarrow q \leftrightarrow \neg q \rightarrow \neg p$

We are now ready to push the notion of tautology a little further. Ordinarily, ascertaining the truth of a statement requires consulting *something other than the statement itself*: either facts about the world or other statements. Take 'The Eiffel Tower is 300 meters tall'. Short of simply accepting it, the only way to directly verify this statement is to travel to Paris and measure the steel spire. In doing so, one would become acquainted with a certain fact about the world, namely the actual height of the tower, which fact could then be compared with the state of affairs asserted by the statement. Alternatively, one might compare the statement with other, more authoritative statements, such as those found in an encyclopedia. It will surely not have escaped the esteemed reader's attention that, in pragmatic terms, the latter procedure is considerably easier to perform. A related method is employed in mathematics where proving a statement involves consulting other statements—most important, the axioms of the mathematical field in question—or previously proved theorems. In any case, what all of the above have in common is that verifying the truth of a statement involves consulting something other than the statement itself. There is considerable controversy over what sorts of verifications are appropriate, but this is the province of so-called theories of truth, which need not concern us any further here. They need not concern us precisely because the appreciation of logical truths is different; it does *not* demand recourse to anything outside the statements themselves, neither facts about the world nor other statements. Tautologies are true in virtue of their particular arrangement of constituent statements, without regard to the meanings of those constituent statements.

But how is it possible that the verification of logical truths requires nothing outside the logical truths themselves? The reason is that logical truths are vacuous, or, more precisely, they cannot be used to assert anything. Their vacuity emerges most clearly by comparison with such "ordinary" statements as 'The Eiffel Tower is 300 meters tall'. The latter statement makes an assertion, something to the effect of, "This is the way things are" or, more pointedly, "Things are thus and not otherwise." The "and not otherwise" gives the statement its determinacy, its assertiveness: the statement rules something out. In particular, a given statement B rules out its opposite, $\neg B$. To persuade ourselves of the truth of such a statement, we must observe that the state of affairs it asserts actually obtains, or conversely, that the state of affairs it excludes does *not* obtain. Logical truths, on the other hand, are missing this "and not otherwise." Someone who asserts $A \vee \neg A$ is not ruling *anything* out, for either A or $\neg A$ must hold—there are no other possibilities (A is assumed to be a statement in the sense of Definition 1.1).[1] In this sense, logical truths do not assert anything. It is thus clear why the meanings of the constituent statements of which a logical truth is composed are irrelevant, for the arrangement of these constituent statements ensures that the statement as a whole *cannot* assert anything, while the constituent statements can go on asserting whatever they please.

The following consideration reinforces the impossibility of asserting anything by means of a logical truth. Assertions are subject to contradiction. Whenever someone claims, "This is the way it is," someone else might claim, "No, that's not the way it is," or "No, it is otherwise." The contradiction itself asserts something that was excluded by the original statement. But since logical truths do not exclude anything, it follows that they cannot be contradicted. How might one go about contradicting Example 2.14, "If the rooster crows on the manure pile, then either the weather will change or it will stay as it is"? The impossibility of contradic-

---

1. Formally speaking, since any statement B excludes $\neg B$, then "$A \vee \neg A$" must exclude "$\neg(A \vee \neg A)$." But as we shall see at the end of section 2.3, this is not really a substantive exclusion.

tion further underscores the status of logical truths as statements that cannot be used to assert anything.

b. The Substitution Theorem

"Theorem" is the name given in mathematics and logic to propositions whose truth is guaranteed by proof. At the end of such a proof one sometimes finds the distinguished abbreviation "QED," which stands for the Latin "quod erat demonstrandum" (that which was to be proved). This signifies that the proof has been concluded. The symbol '∎' may also be used in place of 'QED'. The following theorem allows us to characterize different classes of tautologous formulas as well as to simplify the confirmation of their tautologous status.

The substitution theorem: Let SL formula F contain n distinct sentential letters, $p_1 \ldots p_n$. Let $G_1 \ldots G_n$ be any n SL formulas (both $p_1 \ldots p_n$ and $G_1 \ldots G_n$ have the same number of members, n). Let F' be the formula that results from substituting for every p_i the corresponding G_i (hence the "substitution" in "substitution theorem"). The theorem asserts that if $\vDash F$, then $\vDash F'$.

Example: '$p \vee \neg p$' is a tautology. By the substitution theorem, '$(q \wedge r) \vee \neg (q \wedge r)$' and '$(q \rightarrow r) \vee \neg (q \rightarrow r)$' must also be tautologies, since they can be obtained from '$p \vee \neg p$' by substituting '$(q \wedge r)$' or '$(q \rightarrow r)$' in place of p. More generally, for any SL formula G, $G \vee \neg G$ is a tautology.

Proof of the substitution theorem: We must show that any formula F' meeting the conditions set out above will be true under all possible interpretations. Let any interpretation I' of F' be given. First evaluate the truth values for constituent formulas G_i under I'. The resulting truth analysis of F' will be identical to the analysis of F under the interpretation that assigns to sentential letters p_i the same truth values assigned to the corresponding G_i under I'. Call this interpretation I. But since F is a tautology, it is true under interpretation I. Thus F' is true under any interpretation I'. QED.

When a proposition is easily derived from a theorem, this second proposition is called a "corollary" to the theorem in question. Here is a corollary to the substitution theorem:

Corollary to the substitution theorem: Let SL formula F' represent the particular SF of statement A, in which no connectives have been abstracted away; for every extensionally joined atomic substatement of A, there is a corresponding sentential letter in F'. This formula may be said to represent the "most fine-grained" SF of A. The corollary states that A is a tautology just in case F' is a tautology.

Remark on the value of this corollary: With the corollary in hand, establishing a statement as a tautology now requires that we examine only one SF for the statement, namely the most fine-grained of them. After all, the definition of tautology only required that one SF meet the stated criterion, but it did not say anything about which one was most likely to succeed.

Proof of the corollary: Because of the 'just in case' in the statement of the corollary, its proof requires two parts:

1. Assuming A is a tautology, show that F' is a tautology where F' represents the most fine-grained SF of A. By assumption, A has at least one tautologous SF, call it F. If $F = F'$, the claim is true, and we are done. If $F \neq F'$, then since both formulas arose by abstraction from the same statement A, and since F' is more fine-grained than F, F must contain sentential letters p_i where F' contains particular formulas G_i. But by the substitution theorem, since F is a tautology, F' must also be a tautology.

2. Assuming F' is a tautology, show A is a tautology. This follows immediately from the definition of tautology, since F' is a tautologous SF of A. QED.

2.3. Logical Falsehood

We arrive at our definition of logical falsehood by a path that exactly mirrors our approach to logical truth. The definition is as follows:

Definition 2.10

1. An SF or SL formula is called a "(statement-)logical falsehood" or

"(statement-)logically false" or a "contradiction" or "contradictory," just in case it is false under all extensional interpretations.

2. A statement is called a "(statement-)logical falsehood" or "(statement-) logically false" or a "contradiction" or "contradictory," just in case it has at least one logically false SF.

An example of a logically false formula:

Example 2.18. $p \land \neg p$

Its logical falsehood is evident from the following truth table:

p	$\land$	$\neg$	p
T	**F**	F	T
F	**F**	T	F

The main column contains only Fs. It follows that all statements that have $p \land \neg p$ as one of their logical forms are logically false. These include such patent falsehoods as, "This bread is stale and not stale" and "The concert was pleasant and not pleasant."

The possibility of ascertaining the logical falsehood of a statement without recourse to anything outside the statement itself is a function of the fact that logical falsehoods, like logical truths, cannot be used to assert anything. But although logical falsehoods say nothing, they do it in a different way. In the tautology $A \lor \neg A$, for example, the assertive power of A is neutralized by the addition of the second disjunct, $\neg A$; $A \lor \neg A$ no longer rules anything out and thus no longer asserts anything. By contrast, in the prototype of logical falsehood, $A \land \neg A$, another mechanism is responsible for its nonassertiveness: both A and its contradictory statement are simultaneously asserted, or, in other words, A is asserted and immediately taken back. $A \lor \neg A$ avoids a commitment to A by leaving the choice between A and $\neg A$ open; $A \land \neg A$ avoids a commitment to A by simultaneously insisting on $\neg A$. Of course the attempt to assert $A \land \neg A$ is self-contradictory, since the statement is always false. Anyone who seriously asserts that $A \land \neg A$ (where A is a statement in the sense of Definition 1.1) has thereby demonstrated that he or she has somehow failed to understand what it means to assert a statement in the first place. Statement A excludes $\neg A$, which simply means that $\neg A$ cannot be asserted together with A.

Logical truth and logical falsehood thus differ with regard to the underlying grounds for their respective brands of nonassertiveness. This difference is particularly significant in an older form of logic, so-called classical logic, in which the Law of Non-Contradiction, on which contradictions are to be avoided at all cost, plays a great role. Kant, in particular, considered the Law of Non-Contradiction the very basis of formal logic. But classical logic contains no analogous law on the avoidance of logical truth. The reason is that the logically true variety of nonassertiveness does not result from error but from having left all possibilities open. The nonassertiveness of logical falsehood, however, *does* result from error: the self-destruction of a statement's assertive power.

The three remarks with which we followed our definition of logical truth also apply to logical falsehood, as do corresponding versions of the substitution theorem and its corollary. The following four further remarks also apply to both logical truth and logical falsehood.

1. It may seem strange that while SFs and SL formulas are neither true nor false—their veridicality was abstracted away in obtaining the SFs (compare section II.1.2.b., Remark 2)—some of them are nonetheless tautologous (and thus logically true) or logically false. This is no paradox. Uninterpreted SL formulas are neither true nor false. To attribute statement-logical truth (or falsehood) is to claim that *if* the formula in question were to be interpreted, it would be true (or false) under all interpretations. The concept of the truth of a statement must be strictly distinguished from that of the statement-logical truth (or tautology) of an SF or SL formula.

2. In statement logic, demonstrating that a given statement is tautologous or logically false requires finding one tautologous or logically false SF for the statement. Therefore the claim that a given statement is tautologous (or logically false) cannot be refuted by producing one SF for the statement that fails the test of tautology (or logical falsehood). Such a form may al-

ways be found: p. In principle, refuting such claims demands rather that we examine all of the SFs of the statement in question and show that none of them is tautologous (or logically false). Of course, the task is made considerably easier by the corollary to the substitution theorem, which tells us that examining the most fine-grained SF will decide the issue.

3. Intuitively, the notions of logical truth and logical falsehood are mutually exclusive, since what is logically true cannot be logically false and vice versa. And for SFs and SL formulas, this exclusivity is a straightforward consequence of Definitions 2.9 and 2.10. For whenever the truth analysis of a formula yields truth value T for all possible interpretations, it cannot also yield truth value F for all possible interpretations. To this point the question is trivial. But for *statements,* the mutual exclusivity of logical truth and logical falsehood is *not* obvious, at least as far as Definitions 2.9 and 2.10 are concerned. Might it not happen that while one SF for a given statement was logically true, another was logically false? It must be shown that this cannot occur. The proof follows from the corollary to the substitution theorem: the most fine-grained SF for the statement must be either logically true or logically false, or neither, and thus the statement itself can only be either logically true or logically false, or neither, but never more than one of the above.

4. On the principle that any statement A excludes its opposite, $\neg A$ (compare section II.2.2.a), it is worth asking what, exactly, logical truths and falsehoods exclude. Applying the principle mechanically, the logical truth $A \vee \neg A$ excludes $\neg(A \vee \neg A)$. But $\neg(A \vee \neg A)$ is a logical falsehood, as a truth analysis of $\neg(p \vee \neg p)$ immediately reveals. To assert a logical truth is thus to exclude, or deny, a logical falsehood, something self-contradictory. But since such contradictions exclude themselves, the assertion of a logical truth really excludes nothing. The assertion of a logical truth involves no risk of refutation. Accordingly, someone who asserts a logical truth asserts nothing; the assertion is empty, no assertion at all.

On the other hand, by the same principle, the assertion of a logical falsehood, such as $A \wedge \neg A,$ excludes a logical truth, in this case $\neg(A \wedge \neg A)$.

But logical truths are impossible to exclude or deny, since they are true in and of themselves. Asserting a logical falsehood thus involves the attempt to do the impossible: to deny a logical truth. Accordingly, logical falsehoods cannot be used assertively, and any attempt to do so is self-undermining. The prototype of all logically false statements, $A \wedge \neg A$, illustrates this point perfectly: to simultaneously assert A and $\neg A$ would demonstrate the failure to understand what it means to make an assertion in the first place.

﹡*Exercise 2.14.* Construct truth tables for the following formulas.

1. $(p{\to}q) \wedge p {\to} q$
2. $(p{\to}q) \wedge \neg q {\to} {\to} \neg p$
3. $p \wedge \neg p {\to} q$
4. $p{\to}q \vee \neg q$
5. $(p \wedge q) \wedge \neg q$

2.4. Valid Inference

We are now finally ready to address the central concept of logic, the concept of valid inference or logical consequence. In essence, our procedure will follow the same familiar steps as before: scrutiny of examples, extraction of key features, then finally definition. But some preliminary reflections are called for, since the notion of valid inference comes with new complexities. Given their generality, these reflections will prove useful outside logic, too.

a. Synthetic Definition, Analytic Definition, and Explication

Different contexts, both technical and mundane, entail very different conceptions of what counts as a definition. The systematic classification and analysis of definitions is the province of an entire theoretical discipline, the subtleties of which need not greatly concern us here. For present purposes it will suffice to outline two diametrically opposed kinds of definition, called "synthetic" and "analytic" definition, by means of which we will elucidate the notion of explication.

Synthetic Definition

A "synthetic" or "stipulative" definition is used to construct (or "synthesize") a brand new concept. Definitions 2.4 ("main connective"), 2.6 ("extensional interpretation"), and 2.8 ("truth table of a formula") are all examples of synthetic definitions. The concept of the main column did not exist before someone invented the expression 'main column' to refer to this particular column of the truth table of an SL formula. The primary function of synthetic definitions is thus to introduce abbreviations. It is undoubtedly less cumbersome to say "main column" than "the truth table column below the main connective of the formula," but if we preferred, we *could* get by without the definition for "main column" and always use the longer formulation. Synthetic definitions are special-purpose rules, or conventions. Clearly, rules of this sort cannot be true or false; they are either well- or ill-suited to their given purpose. If the purpose is abbreviation, then they are judged on how well they fulfill it—on how useful the abbreviation is in its designated context.

Analytic Definition

An analytic (or descriptive, or lexical) definition analyzes a previously existing concept by listing its features. It makes explicit the meaning of a concept already in use. For example, if we analyzed the concept "bachelor," we would discover that it includes such features as "unmarried," "not widowed," "not a minor," etc. Packaging this list of features as a definition of "bachelor," we obtain an analytic definition of the concept. (As to the question of whether such definitions are always possible, properly addressing it would take us too far into the philosophy of language.) The primary function of analytic definitions is thus one of clarification: a previously employed but vague concept is made clear and unequivocal by explicitly listing its essential features. An analytic definition may thus be judged as adequate or inadequate by how well it captures a particular linguistic usage. Here, too, it is improper to speak of a definition as true or false; instead, a definition might capture usage more or less adequately.

Synthetic and analytic definitions thus differ both in their primary functions (abbreviation versus clarification) and in the criteria on which they are evaluated (suitability versus adequacy).

Explication

What sort of definition are we after in logic? It turns out that with regard to the most interesting concepts, including validity, logical truth, etc., we are after something in between analytic and synthetic definition. On the one hand, we are piggybacking off conventional usage in an effort to articulate something we somehow already know. For example, we already have an inchoate notion of what counts as a logically valid inference, but we are not yet able to state explicitly what this notion entails. Our vague inklings must be articulated. This is the analytic part of the sort of definition we require. But on the other hand, our vague inklings are not sacrosanct. It may turn out that our preanalytic understanding confuses things that are better off separated, and so any definition will also have to supply correction and clarification. Consider the fact that the use of the word "logical" in the following dialogue has at best a loose connection with the use of the same term in formal logic:

> "What beer can I get you?"
> "Bud Light sounds like the logical choice."

The definition of logically valid inference thus cannot be purely analytic, in which case it would only elucidate prior usage. It must also have a synthetic component, embodying a consensual stipulation. But how should this synthetic component be chosen? It must be chosen in such a way as to ensure that the resulting definition, or *explication,* is a more precise, and, above all, more fruitful tool for the relevant branch of inquiry that was the colloquial concept, with which it nonetheless preserves a certain similarity. Admittedly, this characterization of the requirements for good explication is quite vague, but it will do for our purposes. This vagueness should prepare us for the possibility that a single concept may turn out to have more than one explication. Varying refinements of one and the same colloquial concept may prove equally valuable in virtue of their fruitfulness and similarity to the original concept. Indeed, the existence of a plurality of explications is itself often fruitful. It may be that the notion of logically valid inference may be explicated in more than one way—that we may find more than one definition (in the sense of explication) of the concept in question.

For now, however, this possibility need not concern us. Let us begin our search for an appropriate definition (where, in what follows, "definition" will mean "explication") of the concept of logically valid inference. Toward this end, we must first learn about a practical, if somewhat technical, tool that considerably eases the formulation of explications.

b. Adequacy Criteria

Adequacy criteria are the demands a particular definition (either an explication or an analytic definition) must meet in order to be considered acceptable. The adequacy of a definition in general is understood in terms of the abstract posits of explication listed above. When these posits are refined with a view toward a specific concept, we obtain the adequacy criteria, intermediate steps along the way to an acceptable definition. The formulation of adequacy criteria frequently proceeds by reading characteristic features of the concept to be defined off of typical examples. These features are then assumed to be diagnostic of the concept. We have already followed this procedure, albeit without making it explicit, in arriving at our definitions of tautology and logical falsehood. Once a particular feature has been read off of an example and made into an adequacy criterion, it becomes a *necessary condition* for candidate definitions: a condition any candidate definition must meet, if it is to have a chance of being considered adequate. Ideally, we would find enough such necessary conditions that together they would be sufficient to dictate our construction of the definition. We will soon see whether this ideal can be attained in the definition of logically valid inference. We begin with an example of such an inference, off of which we will read the adequacy criteria for our definition.

Example 2.19. Fred was drunk or on drugs.

Fred was not drunk.

❋

Therefore,   Fred was on drugs.

The first premise is the sort of statement we might find in an arrest report, reflecting the judgment of the officer who witnessed Fred's erratic driving. The 'or' is straightforwardly inclusive. The second premise might be the result of a subsequent blood alcohol test. The conclusion follows from the two premises: if we hold both of them to be true, then we are compelled—compelled in that special way peculiar to logic—to accept the conclusion as likewise true.

In colloquial speech, we often call this kind of inference "valid," "correct," or even "true." But calling it "true" is confusing, since it is unclear whether the term applies to the *inference* in virtue of its validity or simply to the *conclusion,* in which case it asserts only that the statement, 'Fred was on drugs', expresses a fact. As emphasized in section I.1, this distinction is of central importance to logic. The following observations further underscore this point:

a. There are valid inferences with false conclusions.
b. There are valid inferences with true conclusions.
c. There are invalid inferences with true conclusions.
d. There are invalid inferences with false conclusions.

In other words, the validity or invalidity of an inference is independent of the truth or falsity of its conclusion. All four combinations can occur, as the following examples will persuade us.

Combination a: Consider Example 2.19 again, only now assume that Fred's erratic driving results exclusively from an epileptic seizure. Under this assumption, the first premise is false, because both disjuncts are false, and the conclusion is false—but the validity of the inference remains unaffected. Here is an even more extreme example of a valid inference with false premises and false conclusion:

Example 2.20. All circles are square.

Some triangles are circles.

*

Therefore,   Some triangles are square.

After observing the validity of this inference, Friedhelm Moser, in his book *Der philosophische Flohmarkt* (The Philosophical Flea Market) remarked, "It's a wonder that logicians don't all end up in locked asylums" (p. 92).

Combination b: Example 2.19, assuming the premises are true.

Combination c:

Example 2.21. If it is raining, the street is wet.

It is not raining.

*

Therefore,   The street is not wet.

The invalidity of this inference is immediately apparent once we appreciate the fact that the first premise only describes the street conditions *if* it is raining. But the second premise disputes this condition. It follows that taken together, the two premises yield absolutely no information on current street conditions, and so the conclusion fails to follow from the premises. It is easy to imagine a situation in which, while both premises are true, the street is still wet—as when a street-cleaning machine has just past or a broken water main has left it flooded. Even if the street is in fact dry, this possibility is enough to show that the inference is invalid. So, inference 2.21 is invalid, even if the conclusion is true.

Combination d: Example 2.21, assuming the street has been soaked by an overturned soft drink delivery truck.

Given the demonstrable independence of "valid inference" and "true conclusion," the ambiguous phrase "true inference" must always be avoided and the adjective 'true' applied only to statements, never to relationships among statements. Formal logic is not concerned with the truth of statements (leaving aside logical truth), but rather with the validity of inferential relationships.

Having reminded ourselves once more of the concept we are attempting to define, more or less analytically, we are in a position to articulate the adequacy criteria for a definition of the statement-logical concept of validity. We return to our example of valid inference:

Example 2.19.   Fred was drunk or on drugs.

Fred was not drunk.

*

Therefore,   Fred was on drugs.

What is it, exactly, that makes the move from premises to conclusion so compelling? Clearly it is the fact that while the first premise asserts that (at least) one of two possibilities must hold, the second excludes one, leaving the other. It is this second possibility that is asserted in the conclusion. It is thus part of the "mechanism" of the inference that the first disjunct of the first premise is repeated (but negated) in the second premise, leaving the second disjunct to be repeated affirmatively in the conclusion. The compelling appeal of the inference must rest on this *repeated occurrence* of constituent statements. Let us formulate this insight as our first adequacy criterion:

Criterion 1. The validity of the inference depends on the repeated occurrence of particular constituent statements.

A further piece of the mechanism of 2.19 is the fact that the two constituent statements of the first premise are joined by the connective 'or' (this is what led us to say that the first premise articulated two possibilities), while the second premise contains the connective 'not' (which is what led us to say that one of the two possibilities had been excluded). The appeal of the move from premises to conclusion must also reside in the particular connectives occurring in the premises (and perhaps also in the conclusion). We have our second adequacy criterion:

Criterion 2. The validity of the inference depends on the particular connectives occurring in it.

It is easily seen that the validity of the inference has nothing to do with the specific meanings of the repeated constituent statements; we recall making an analogous observation in our discussion of logical truth. We can persuade ourselves of the irrelevance of these meanings by replacing the constituent statements with abbreviations. The substitution in no way detracts from the appeal of the inference:

Example 2.22. A_1 or A_2

Not A_1

*

Therefore, A_2

Our third adequacy criterion thus becomes:

Criterion 3. The validity of the inference is independent of the meanings of the constituent statements occurring in it.

Up to now we have been content to articulate one or another factor on which the validity of an inference depends or fails to depend. It is time we were clear on what this validity actually consists in. Validity consists in nothing other than truth transfer, familiar from our introduction (section I.1, Feature 1). In positive terms, successful truth transfer means that the truth of the premises guarantees the truth of the conclusion; in negative terms, it means that true premises never coincide with a false conclusion. The validity of an inference thus rules out a particular *combination* of truth values: "true" for all of the premises (or, what amounts to the same thing, for the *conjunction* of all those premises) and "false" for the conclusion. This leads us to our fourth and final adequacy criterion:

Criterion 4. The validity of an inference demands truth transfer; in other words, a true conjunction of premises can never coincide with a false conclusion.

Criterion 4 has to do with the particular *correlation* of truth values for premises and conclusion permitted by valid inference. This is the most important of our adequacy criteria, and in other discussions of valid inference, it is frequently the only one to be cited explicitly. By itself, Criterion 4 is not, however, enough to allow us to distinguish the different *kinds* of valid inference to which the various branches of logic are devoted, for *all* valid inferences satisfy this criterion. Only with the help of Criteria 1–3 may we zero in on the particular valid inferences with which we are presently concerned: the valid inferences of statement logic.

c. Further Refinements of the Adequacy Criteria?

1. Falsehood Transfer

In the next section we will distill our adequacy conditions down to a definition of statement-logical validity. But first, however, we must deal with one more potential concern. At first blush, it appears a further adequacy criterion might be called for, one which requires falsehood transfer.

> **Criterion 5.** The validity of an inference demands falsehood transfer; a false conjunction of premises can never coincide with a true conclusion.

Or we might instead envision a weaker version of Criterion 5, one which required the transfer of falsehood from premises to conclusion only when *all* of the premises were false; as stated, Criterion 5 applies when only *one* premise is false, since this is enough to falsify the conjunction. But there is no need to decide between the two versions of the falsehood transfer criterion; both must be rejected. Consider the following example:

> **Example 2.23.**   If Fido is a dog, then Fido is a vegetarian.
> If Fido is a vegetarian, then Fido likes chasing cats.
>
> ＊
> Therefore,   If Fido is a dog, then Fido likes chasing cats.

In this case there can be no doubt that the conjunction of premises is false, since *both* premises are false: dogs are not vegetarians, so Fido is not one either, and vegetarians are not usually in the habit of chasing cats. But the conclusion might easily embody a true statement about Fido. What about the validity of the inference? So as not to be confused by the peculiar statements in Example 2.23, let us replace constituent statements by convenient abbreviations. The inference then becomes:

Example 2.23a. If *D*, then *V*.
If *V*, then *C*.
*
Therefore, If *D*, then *C*.

Since this inference has every appearance of validity, the original, 2.23, must also be valid. Despite its validity, we note there has been no falsehood transfer from premises to conclusion.

What should we do? On the one hand, Example 2.23 (and 2.23a) are intuitively valid. But since both premises are false, and their conjunction thus doubly false, the validity of the example contradicts our proposed Criterion 5—both versions! Something must go: either Criterion 5 or the validity of Example 2.23. In order to make a *reasoned* decision on which to discard, we must take a closer look at the "mechanism" whereby the true conclusion follows—or appears to follow—from the false premises.

And on careful inspection, the validity of 2.23a really does appear unassailable. It arises in the following way: If *D* holds, then *V* must also hold. If *V* holds, then so does *C*. So if *D* holds, then via the intermediate step *V*, we obtain *C*. Therefore, if *D*, then *C*. Now it becomes clear how this inference can validly produce a true conclusion from false premises: it does so just in case the moves from *D* to *V* and from *V* to *C* are unacceptable, while going from *D* to *C* remains permissible. This true conclusion no longer bears any trace of the illicit moves; all reference to *V* has been swallowed. We have now discovered a method for generating a whole class of valid inferences with false premises and true conclusion. First pick a true statement of the form 'If *A*, then *C*' as your conclusion. Then select a statement *B* that ensures that 'If *A*, then *B*' and 'If *B*, then *C*' are both false. The two false conditionals will be the premises of your valid inference, and the true one will be its conclusion.

Our reasoning leads us to the following result: Both versions of the demand that valid inferences enforce falsehood transfer from premises to conclusion are *inadequate*. We will not accept Criterion 5 into our list of adequacy criteria. Later on, however, we will be called upon to question the completeness of this list once again (see section II.2.4.f).

d. Definition

We are now ready to distill our adequacy criteria down into a definition of statement-logical validity. We proceed in two steps.

Step 1: First we summarize Criteria 1–3. Together, they assert that validity depends on connectives and on the repeated occurrence of constituent statements and that it is independent of the meanings of these statements. But this is the same as saying that the validity of an inference depends only on appropriate statement forms of premises and conclusions and not on any other features of these statements—especially not on their meanings. It depends on "appropriate" statement forms, because only for those SFs of premises and conclusion in which the connectives, and the repeated occurrence of constituent statements, have not been completely abstracted away will the validity of the inference remain apparent. (Anyone needing a refresher on the notion of a statement form should turn back to section II.1.2, Definition 2.1.) Needless to say, every valid inference also has SFs in which its validity is *not* expressed. For example, every valid inference with two distinct premises and a conclusion distinct from both of them has the following SF:

$$p$$
$$q$$
$$*$$
$$r$$

In this SF, the pattern of connectives and repeated constituent statements—the pattern that is so characteristic of our guiding example, 2.19—has been lost.

It is plain that the very idea of a statement form is tailor-made for the first three of our adequacy criteria. The dividing line between form and content can be drawn in such a way as to leave everything relevant to the validity of an inference in an SF, while the residual content of the statements is abstracted away.

Step 2: By Step 1, the grounds for the validity of an inference may be found in appropriate SFs of premises and conclusion. Let such SFs be given. We will use 'A' as an abbreviation for the SF of the conjunction of the premises, and 'B' for the SF of the conclusion. We must now articulate the feature of A and B that is decisive for the validity of the inference, such that if A and B have the feature in question, the inference is automatically valid. Further, if they lack this decisive factor, then any potential validity must rest on something other than SFs A and B.

We return to Criterion 4, which prohibits a true conjunction of premises from coinciding with a false conclusion. We encounter the following apparent paradox: On the one hand, Criterion 4 excludes a particular combination of truth values for the conjunction of premises and the conclusion. But on the other hand, our analysis of Criteria 1–3 revealed that the validity of an inference rests exclusively on appropriate SFs, such as A and B. The problem is that SFs are neither true nor false, and so once premises and conclusion have been abstracted to the level of SFs, it is impossible to ask after their truth values, let alone after the relevant pattern of truth values. Here we must call on the notion of extensional interpretation, whose proper function in logic will now become apparent. It is possible to rearticulate certain requirements on the *truth values of statements* in terms of the *extensional interpretations of appropriate SFs* for these statements. For Criterion 4, this possibility is cashed out as follows.

Criterion 4 demands that a true conjunction of premises never coincides with a false conclusion. On the level of statement forms, on which the validity of an inference can be expressed in terms of SFs A and B, this demand can be reformulated:

Criterion 4.1. The extensional interpretations on which A is true must also make B true.

Whenever Criterion 4.1 is satisfied, Criterion 4 must necessarily also be satisfied, since the conjunction of premises is an intensional interpretation of A, and the conclusion an intensional interpretation of B.

I now offer a somewhat more artificial formulation of Criterion 4.1. As will become clear later on, this reworking will help pave the way toward our definitive version of Criterion 4.

Criterion 4.2. The formula $A \wedge \neg B$ must not be true on any extensional interpretation.

Criterion 4.2 is equivalent to 4.1, for if there were an interpretation on which $A \wedge \neg B$ was true, this same interpretation would have to make both A and $\neg B$ true, or A true and B false. This, of course, is precisely what 4.1 rules out. Alternatively, Criterion 4.2 might be expressed as the following:

Criterion 4.3. The formula $A \wedge \neg B$ must be false on all extensional interpretations.

Or in positive terms:

Criterion 4.4. The formula $\neg(A \wedge \neg B)$ must be true on all extensional interpretations.

But since $\neg(A \wedge \neg B)$ is the same as $A \rightarrow B$—we recall that this was the way we introduced the conditional in the first place—4.4 becomes:

Criterion 4.5. $A \rightarrow B$ must be true on all extensional interpretations.

But by Definition 2.9, SL formulas that are true on all extensional interpretations are *tautologies*. So the end result of our second step is simply

Criterion 4.6. $A \rightarrow B$ must be a tautology.

Since $A \rightarrow B$ is just an SF of the statement "Conjunction of premises $\rightarrow$ Conclusion," then when the former is a tautology, the latter must be, too.

We are now finally ready for our definition of statement-logical validity. It has two parts, the first geared toward formulas, the second toward statements.

Definition 2.11.

1. The inference from one SL formula A to a second, B, is said to be (statement-logically) valid just in case $A{\rightarrow}B$ is a tautology.

2. The inference from a set of premises to a conclusion is said to be (statement-) logically valid just in case "Conjunction of premises$\rightarrow$Conclusion" is a tautology.

Valid inferences are sometimes also called "correct" or "deductively valid." Inferences themselves are sometimes called "consequences" or "implications" (though see Remark 2 in subsection 2.4.e). An inference or chain of inferences is frequently referred to as an "argument." When there is a valid inference from A to B, or from a set of premises to a conclusion, we also say that A *implies* B or that the premises *imply* the conclusion. The conclusion, in turn, is said to be a "logical consequence" of the premises.

It should be noted that the second part of Definition 2.11 requires that we first establish the tautologous status of an SF of the statement "Conjunction of premises$\rightarrow$Conclusion." Now, one might try to construct such an SF, $A{\rightarrow}B$, by first abstracting A as an SF for the conjunction of the premises, then *independently* choosing an SF B for the conclusion. But testing an SF derived in this way will not work, since its construction has not taken into account the repeated occurrence of constituent statements in both premises *and* conclusion. But such repetition is a key component of the mechanism of valid inference (see Criterion 1).

A simple trick allows us to combine the two parts of 2.11 into a single definition:

Definition 2.11′. Let A and B be statements or SL formulas. The inference from A to B is called "statement-logically valid" just in case $A{\rightarrow}B$ is a tautology.

The trick consists in the fact that Definition 2.11´ actually implicitly makes reference to two different kinds of tautology, since this notion is defined differently for statements and for SL formulas. If $A \rightarrow B$ is an SL formula, then for it to be a tautology is for it to be true on all extensional interpretations. But if $A \rightarrow B$ is a statement, then it is tautologous just in case it has at least one tautologous SF. This way of unifying two genuinely distinct metalogical definitions, one for formulas and another for statements, will find repeated application in discussions to follow.

The symbol '$\vDash$' is used as an abbreviation for validity; '$A \vDash B$' is typically read as 'B may be validly inferred from A' or 'B is a logical consequence of A', where A and B may be either statements or SL formulas. This use of the symbol '$\vDash$' is completely consistent with its use in designating logical truth. '$A \vDash B$' means that the truth of B is guaranteed by the truth of A, while '$\vDash B$' means simply that the truth of B is guaranteed by itself, without any other presuppositions.

Let us consider the application of our definition to a concrete example, the familiar 2.19, used in discovering our adequacy criteria:

Example 2.19. Fred was drunk or on drugs.

Fred was not drunk.

*

Therefore,   Fred was on drugs.

The conversion of 2.19 into 2.21 by means of abbreviations should also be familiar:

Example 2.21. A_1 or A_2

Not A_1

*

Therefore, A_2

Applied to this example, the conjunction of premises referred to in Definition 2.11 is $(A_1 \vee A_2) \wedge \neg A_1$, and the conclusion is A_2. Our definition now invites us to consider an SF for the statement $((A_1 \vee A_2) \wedge \neg A_1) \rightarrow A_2$. An SF in which all of the connectives are preserved is close at hand: $((p \lor q) \land \neg p) \to q$. Now we must test this SF to determine if it is a tautology. The truth table for the formula is as follows:

$((p \lor q) \land \neg p) \to q$

T	T	T	**T**	T
T	F F F	T	**T**	F
F	T	F	**T**	T
F F	F F	F	**T**	F

Plainly, the formula is tautologous—exactly as we expected. (It will be noted that in the interests of parsimony I have omitted some of the truth values from this table. Those omitted on a given row are all unnecessary for determining the truth value entered in the main column of that row. If we begin filling in the table from the right, it is clear than for any row on which the consequent of the conditional is true, there is no need to establish the truth value of the antecedent; the conditional itself will be true regardless.)

e. Supplementary Remarks on the Definition of Statement-Logical Validity

1. The two parts of Definition 2.11 are significantly different in character. The first part, which defines validity for SL *formulas,* is a *synthetic* definition. It introduces a new concept as an abbreviated description of a particular relationship among formulas. By contrast, when it comes to statements, we already have a prior understanding of validity and occasionally talk of the validity or invalidity of inferences even in everyday speech. As anticipated at the end of section II.2.4.a, the second part of Definition 2.11 is thus an explication of a concept already in use. The first part of the definition should thus be evaluated on whether the abbreviation it introduces is useful, while for the second we must ask if the explication is adequate (we will return to this question in section II.2.4.f.). Given its hybrid character, our compressed Definition 2.11′, is at odds with it-

self and potentially enormously misleading, since for formulas it offers a synthetic definition of validity, whereas for statements it offers an explication of the same term. This is yet another reason why it is essential to distinguish statements from the logical forms of statements.

2. It is important to respect the difference between the conditional and the relation of valid inference. Confusing the two is made easier by the fact that the word 'implication' is sometimes used for both: 'material implication' for the conditional, and 'logical implication' for valid inference. But the conditional—which itself occurs in the definition of valid inference—is a sentential connective. It unites two constituent statements to form a new statement and is thus a piece of object-language. But valid inference is no connective. It is a metalevel relation between object-level statements.

3. According to Definition 2.11, demonstrating the validity of an inference requires testing the tautologous status of the statement "Conjunction of premises → Conclusion." In the interests of expediting the test, rather than examining a range of SFs for this statement, one may go directly to the most fine-grained of them. By the corollary to the substitution theorem (section 2.2.b), a statement is tautologous just in case its most fine-grained SF is tautologous.

4. The explicit definition of statement-logical validity is the culmination of our introduction to statement logic, the goal toward which everything up to this point has been prepared. This definition finally justifies some of the claims made previously:

* Because the compelling appeal of statement-logically valid inference depends on it, it makes sense to insist that the sameness and difference of statements belong to statement form.
* For the same reason, the extensional connectives should also be assigned to statement form.
* Because the conditional is needed in order to define valid inference, it makes sense to introduce this connective in the way here proposed.

* The same reason also justifies our attention to the extensional interpretation and truth analysis of SL formulas.
* Finally, the same reason justifies our introduction of logical truth and tautology prior to the definition of statement-logical validity.

5. Definition 2.11 deepens our understanding of valid inference. By this definition, the validity of an inference from statement A to statement B is equivalent to the tautologous status of $A{\rightarrow}B$. To dispute the validity of an inference that satisfies this definition, one must thus *deny* that $A{\rightarrow}B$ is a tautology. But that would amount to resisting the irresistible truth of a statement satisfying the definition of tautology, Definition 2.9. Imagine someone who disputed the validity of Example 2.21:

Example 2.21. A_1 or A_2
Not A_1
*
Therefore, A_2

Rejecting this example would mean denying the truth of a statement of the same type as $B{\vee}{\neg}B$ (in this case $(A_1{\vee}A_2){\wedge}{\neg}A_1{\rightarrow}A_2)$), a statement whose truth follows conclusively from its structure alone. Put in positive terms, to acknowledge the compelling appeal of valid inferences is to acknowledge the peculiar veridical character of statements whose truth rests on nothing outside the statements themselves, while mere garden-variety truths rest on *external* facts or *other* statements (compare section II.2.2a.).

6. Statement logic recognizes two particularly important kinds of valid inference, still known by their Latin names: *modus ponens* and *modus tollens*. Modus ponens (also called *modus ponendo ponens*), or "affirming the antecedent," allows us to infer the conclusion B from premises $A{\rightarrow}B$ and A. It is called "affirming the antecedent" because it involves two premises, one a conditional statement and the other the affirmation of the antecedent of the conditional. What is inferred is, of course, the consequent

of the conditional. To prove the validity of modus ponens, we need only demonstrate that '$((p{\to}q)\land p){\to}q$' is a tautology (see Exercise 2.14). Modus tollens allows us to infer $\neg A$ from premises $A{\to}B$ and $\neg B$, and it is valid because '$((p{\to}q)\land\neg q){\to}\neg p$' is a tautology (again, see Exercise 2.14). Modus tollens is of great importance in Sir Karl Popper's philosophy of science, known as "critical rationalism" or "falsificationism." Roughly speaking, the falsification of a hypothesis A consists in first showing that it implies a particular observable consequence B—that $A{\to}B$ is logically true—and then demonstrating empirically that B is false or that $\neg B$ is true. By modus tollens, we may infer $\neg A$: A has been falsified on grounds of the empirical datum $\neg B$.

7. Other valid inferences may be drawn from one, three, or more premises. We will encounter one such example at the beginning of the next section.

❋*Exercise 2.15*

1. Formulate a conclusion that may be validly inferred from the following two premises and show that the resulting inference is statement-logically valid:

a. If stupidity can be learned, then there are many diligent students.

b. If there are many diligent students, then teachers are content.

2. An argument from Descartes's *Meditations* VI may be reconstructed as follows:

By its nature, the body is divisible.
If body and soul are one and the same, then the soul is divisible.
But by its nature, the soul is indivisible.
Therefore, body and soul are not one and the same.
Test this argument for statement-logical validity.

3. Using the tools of statement logic, evaluate the following argument concerning the foundations of ethics.

If subjectivism or utilitarianism is correct, ethical concepts are reducible to empirical concepts.

But neither of these positions is correct.

Therefore, ethical concepts are not reducible to empirical concepts.

4. Using the tools of statement logic, evaluate the following argument, paraphrased from a 1995 advertisement in the *Neue Zürcher Zeitung (NZZ)*:

He who reads the *NZZ*

> has broad horizons.
> He who has broad horizons
> takes the high ground.
> He who takes the high ground
> is incorruptible.
> He who is incorruptible
> is a good climber.
> He who is a good climber
> never falls off the wagon.
> He who never falls off the wagon

is never hung over.

٭*Exercise 2.16.* Determine whether one of the following sentences implies the other:

a. The company is required to pay compensatory damages if and only if it is a corporation and was founded no later than 1989.

b. If the company is a corporation, then it was founded no later than 1989 and is required to pay compensatory damages; and if the company is not a corporation, then it was founded after 1989, and it is not required to pay compensatory damages.

f. Further Refinements of the Adequacy Criteria?

2. The So-Called Paradoxes of Implication

In section II.2.4.c, we considered whether our list of four adequacy criteria, understood as a set of demands to be placed on any satisfactory explication of valid inference, ought not to be expanded. There our question concerned the wisdom of accepting falsehood transfer as a characteristic of valid inference, and over the course of our discussion, we concluded it was undoubtedly *not* such a characteristic. Now we must evaluate another candidate addition to our list of adequacy criteria. Consider the following example:

> *Example 2.24.* The forest is green and the forest is not green.
>
>   *
>
> Therefore,   Tomorrow is Christmas.

Notice that by Definition 2.11, this example constitutes a statement-logically valid inference, because '$p \wedge \neg p \rightarrow q$' is a tautology (see Exercise 2.14). Similar considerations apply in the following case:

> *Example 2.25.* Tomorrow is Easter.
>
>   *
>
> Therefore,   There either are or are not environmental problems.

Again, this inference satisfies Definition 2.11, since '$p \rightarrow q \vee \neg q$' is a tautology (Exercise 2.14). Inferences like 2.24 and 2.25 are often called "paradoxes of implication," because while we would not automatically recognize them as valid (after all, premise and conclusion have nothing to do with one another), the canons of classical logic demand that we treat them as such.

Logicians differ widely on how to handle inferences of this sort. Some see them as paradoxical in only a relatively harmless sense: though these inferences violate our *pre-reflective* expectations regarding valid inference, more careful scrutiny allows us to accept their classification as valid in formal logic. But for others, these inferences demonstrate a fundamental limitation of so-called classical (statement) logic. They claim that the inadequacies thus revealed can only be overcome by replacing classical logic with a better theory. In order to understand the two positions, let us have a closer look at the ways in which Example 2.24 and 2.25 satisfy Definition 2.11.

In 2.24, the premise is a logical falsehood: "The forest is green and the forest is not green." By Definition 2.11, this immediately yields a valid inference, since a conditional with a false antecedent is always true, regardless of the truth value of the consequent. Now it becomes clear why despite the fourth adequacy criterion, on which true premises can never coincide with a false conclusion (section II.2.4.b), Example 2.24 still qualifies as a valid inference under our definition: Criterion 4 is not violated, because in 2.24 there is no way for the premise ever to be true. In the Middle Ages, such inferences led to the principle "ex falso quodlibet" (though strictly, it should have been "ex contradictione quodlibet"): anything follows from a contradiction.

Similar considerations apply in the case of 2.25. Here the conclusion is a logical truth: "There either are or are not environmental problems." By Definition 2.11, the validity of the inference immediately follows, since a conditional with a true consequent is always true, regardless of the truth value of the antecedent. Example 2.25 satisfies our definition because the combination forbidden by our fourth adequacy criterion can never occur, given the logical truth of the conclusion. The truth values of the premises are irrelevant.

A diagnosis for the tension between our pre-reflective skepticism and the classification of 2.24 and 2.25 as valid inferences in accordance with Definition 2.11 is now at hand. Because the premise of 2.24 is logically false, the corresponding conditional is logically true. But of course there is no truth transfer from premise to conclusion. In 2.25, the truth of the conclusion is completely independent of the truth value of the premise, leaving us equally disinclined to classify the inference as valid. According to our pre-reflective understanding of validity, a valid inference involves truth *transfer,* in which the supposed truth of the premises is *transferred* to the conclusion. This requires some sort of connection between the meanings of premises and conclusion. In both of the cases currently under consideration, there *is* no such truth transfer from premises to conclusion, since the meanings of the two are entirely unrelated.

This diagnosis leaves us with two options. The first option requires that we be prepared to revise our pre-reflective understanding of validity, on which 2.24 and 2.25 were invalid. In support of such revision, one might argue that these inferences were not actually excluded by our pre-reflective intuitions; they simply were not covered by them. In both cases, the success or failure of truth transfer simply is not an issue; the satisfaction of Criterion 4 is guaranteed not by the correlation between the truth values of premise and conclusion, but by the truth value of premise or conclusion alone. Strictly speaking, Definition 2.11 does not actually conflict with our intuitions—it merely decides the validity of cases on which we had no pre-reflective intuitions in the first place. We must simply become used to the fact that formal logic treats such cases decisively. For our willingness to accept it, we are rewarded with a relatively simple, transparent theory of valid inference.

But the second option insists that we must not give up on the notion that truth *transfer* is part of every valid inference. On this approach, simply accepting the so-called paradoxes of implication as given would be utterly misguided. The fundamental problem with Definition 2.11 is that its satisfaction does *not* guarantee truth transfer. In Example 2.24, there cannot be any sort of truth transfer from premise to conclusion, since the premise cannot be true, being a logical falsehood. Nor is there any truth transfer in Example 2.25, since irrespective of the truth of the premise, the conclusion is true *anyway*, being a logical truth. By contrast, consider example 2.19: "Fred was drunk or on drugs. Fred was not drunk. Therefore, Fred was on drugs." As we established earlier, the compelling appeal of the move from premises to conclusion derives among other things from the repeated occurrence of constituent statements (section II.2.4.b). In 2.19, this repetition constitutes a *connection* between the meanings of premises and conclusion. Examples 2.24 and 2.25 also contain repeated occurrences of constituent statements: "The forest is green" and "There are environmental problems," respectively. But in 2.24, "The forest is green" occurs both times in the premise, while in 2.25 "There are environmental problems" occurs both times in the conclusion. It is this pattern of repetition, combined with negation, that allows the two examples to satisfy Definition 2.11, since this is how the logical falsehood in 2.24 and the logical truth in 2.25 are put together. But repetition of this sort does not engender the sort of *connection* between premise and conclusion found in Example 2.19.

On our second option, then, Examples 2.24 and 2.25 must be classified as invalid, since they lack the meaningful connectedness of premises and conclusion indispensable to genuine truth transfer. But how is this possible, given that Definition 2.11 was the result of a careful discussion of adequacy criteria? The only possible culprit is our formulation of Criterion 4: "The validity of an inference demands truth transfer; in other words, a true conjunction of premises can never coincide with a false conclusion" (section II.2.4.b). But our second option forces us to understand truth transfer as involving something more than just the impossibility of true premises coinciding with a false conclusion, since although this impossibility is given for both 2.24 and 2.25, neither exhibits truth transfer. The solution to our present trouble is thus *not* to add new adequacy criteria. Rather we should avoid identifying the truth transfer requirement with the prohibition against combining true premises with false conclusion, where this identification is implied by the "in other words" in our formulation of Criterion 4. What our second option demands is that we correct Criterion 4. It might read as follows:

Criterion 4*. The validity of an inference demands truth transfer, or in other words:

    1. True premises must never coincide with a false conclusion; and
    2. There is some connection between the meanings of premises and conclusion.

Criterion 4* is hardly very specific, as it leaves it entirely open what we should take as "some connection between the meanings of premises and conclusion." But this somewhat vague formulation has been chosen deliberately, as the precise nature of the desired connection remains one of the basic problems of logic for which there is no generally agreed-upon solution. Discussion of this problem has been particularly heated in recent decades, but unfortunately without definitive resolution. Consequently, it has not proved possible to incorporate Criterion 4* in a consensual definition of valid inference. Essentially, there are two ways we might improve on our present definition. We might attempt to *supplement* the definition by adding new conditions to require a connection between premises and conclusion, thus guaranteeing genuine truth transfer. This way leads to "complex logic." Alternatively—and this is the path most often taken—we might dispense with the use of the conditional in our definition of validity. For the root cause of our difficulties is the *extensionality* of the conditional. $A \rightarrow B$ is true whenever either A is false or B is true, regardless of whether there is any connection between the meanings of A and B. In this regard the *material* conditional departs from our ordinary understanding of "if . . . then" statements. In response, there have been attempts to capture statements of the form "If A, then B" using nonextensional connectives. Such candidates are often called "strict" or "relevant" implication, to distinguish them from the material implication of the familiar conditional. But at present there is still no consensus on how best to explicate the sort of "if . . . then" relation that connects the premises and conclusion of an inference. The literature is replete with competing explicatory proposals.

Such proposals frequently proceed by first identifying inferences that, though classified as valid by traditional statement logic, nonetheless violate our intuitions on validity. These become the test cases on which new attempts to define validity must be evaluated; the candidate definitions of the new logic must classify them as invalid. The most intractable disputes among logicians center around such cases. I would like to defend the following position: The inference in 2.24, which exemplifies the principle that "anything follows from a contradiction," is invalid precisely because *nothing* may be inferred from $A \wedge \neg A$ (except $A \wedge \neg A$ itself, or some other logical falsehood). In particular, *neither A* nor ¬*A* may be inferred from this statement, let alone any arbitrary *B*. This claim is perhaps startling, because the inference from *A*∧¬*A* to *A* is just a special case of the inference from *A*∧*B* to *A*, and the validity of the latter has not yet been disputed. How could it be? If the truth of *A and B* is asserted, the inference to the truth of *A* (or the truth of *B*) is assured! In fact it is not my intention to challenge this inference, only to limit its applicability to cases in which *B* is distinct from ¬*A* (for atomic *A* and *B*). Thus, the claim is that nothing follows from *A*∧¬*A*, not even *A* itself (the only statement that can be inferred from *A*∧¬*A* is *A*∧¬*A* itself, or some other logical falsehood). How might this claim be defended?

One way draws on the following intuition: the premises of a valid inference must at least be *potentially* true. I have to be able to *think* of them as true—however counterfactual that assumption might be—in order to determine to which other statements their supposed truth necessarily transfers. On this intuition, the potential truth of the premises is a necessary condition for the validity of inferences. But the potential truth of the premises is not part of Definition 2.11, and Example 2.24 shamelessly exploits this "loophole." Its premise is, after all, a logical falsehood, whose truth we cannot even *attempt* to presuppose, not even in order to determine what, counterfactually, would follow from it.

A second way draws on the depiction of logical falsehood at the end of section II.2.3. There it was claimed that logical falsehoods are statements with which no assertions can be made. If this characterization is accepted, then the inference rule "*A* may be inferred from *A*∧¬*A*" implies that the statement *A*, which may indeed be used to assert something (provided it is not itself a logical truth or falsehood), can be inferred from a statement with which nothing may be asserted. Or, in other words, the potentially informative statement *A* can be derived from the absolutely uninformative statement *A*∧¬*A*. But this contradicts the generally accepted view that valid inferences are not themselves *ampliative;* the conclusion of a valid inference can never contain more than what was already contained—more or less explicitly—in the premises. How else could valid inferences prove so compelling? Now, if the premise of a given inference is a statement so constructed that it cannot be used to actually assert anything, it is hard to see how the conclusion of that same inference could be used in making an assertion. The conclusion would have acquired some qualitatively new feature, which, since the premise lacks it, could not have been transferred in the inference. Rather than accepting the inference from $A \wedge \neg A$ to A (or $\neg A$), it strikes me as much more plausible that in the logical falsehood $A \wedge \neg A$, the conjuncts A and $\neg A$ mutually annihilate or neutralize each other, so that *neither one* can be inferred from $A \wedge \neg A$.

It should be acknowledged that my proposal that we allow nothing to be inferred from $A \wedge \neg A$ except $A \wedge \neg A$ itself (or some other logical falsehood) is quite radical. After all, the inference from $A \wedge \neg A$ to A is a special case of the inference from $A \wedge B$ to A, and the validity of the latter is absolutely unimpeachable. Why should substituting $\neg A$ in place of B change anything in this regard? By the above analysis, this substitution is singular in the following sense: it destroys a property a statement of the form $A \wedge B$ would otherwise possess, namely its assertive power. In virtue of this singularity, substituting $\neg A$ in place of B has the result of drastically reducing the set of logical consequences of $A \wedge B$—the set of statements that may be validly inferred from $A \wedge B$.

Perhaps the following analogy will serve to soften somewhat the apparent radicalism of this proposal. In the domain of real numbers, the division of one real number by another yields a well-defined result, except in one singular case, namely the division by zero. Thus, a perfectly well-behaved operation, division, is forbidden for one singular case. According to my proposal, by analogy, the inference from $A \wedge B$ to A is perfectly valid, except for one singular case, when B equals $\neg A$.

The following objection will be raised against this proposal.[2] If we accept that nothing may be inferred from a logical falsehood (save for the

---

2. This was raised to me in discussion with Stephen Read.

logical falsehood itself or some other logical falsehood), then we lose a method crucial to proof procedures in mathematics and elsewhere, the method of indirect proof. Briefly, indirect proof proceeds by assuming, as one of our premises, the exact opposite of what we are trying to prove. The next step is to show that, taken together, this set of premises allows us to infer some self-contradictory consequence. It follows that the claim we are trying to prove must follow from the original set of premises. Schematically, this works as follows: Let P be the conjunction of premises to be used in the proof, and C the claim to be proved. Indirect proof succeeds when from $P \land \neg C$ we infer a contradiction, say $A \land \neg A$. But $(P \land \neg C) \models (A \land \neg A)$ can only hold if $P \land \neg C$ is itself contradictory, which in turn implies that $\neg(P \land \neg C)$ must be logically true. But then it must be the case that $P \models C$—that the claim to be proved is a logical consequence of the premises. For present purposes, what matters is that indirect proof involves an inference from contradictory assumptions, which appears to be prohibited by the proposal that only logical falsehoods can be inferred from $A \land \neg A$. But appearances are deceiving. Let us take some complex statement or SL formula A, where A may or may not be a logical falsehood. Now suppose that we begin to draw inferences from A, in accordance with the rules of valid inference, but *without taking into account the possibility that A might be a logical falsehood*. Eventually, we discover that our rules of inference allow us to infer both B and $\neg B$ from A. It follows from this turn of events that A must be a logical falsehood, for if it were not, it could not have $B \land \neg B$ as a consequence. But this is precisely the result furnished by indirect proof. On the view being defended here, inferring A from $A \land B$ is invalid when $B = \neg A$. But there is nothing wrong with inferring A from $A \land B$ when it is not known whether $B = \neg A$. If no contradiction results (or, strictly, if no contradiction *can* result), then the inference is certainly valid. If a contradiction does result, the inference must be invalid, but it has nonetheless served its purpose in the context of indirect proof by revealing the contradictory character of the premises. Indirect proof is thus consistent with our proposal, though it is interpreted somewhat differently. On the traditional view, when B is inferred from A, it does not matter if A is a logical falsehood; if it is, then in addition to inferring B, we may also infer $\neg B$. On our proposal, however, we must first determine if A is a logical falsehood. If it is, then neither B nor $\neg B$ may be inferred from A (though $B \wedge \neg B$ may).

It is time to draw this discussion of controversial issues to a close. But we must still ask whether the version of statement logic developed here is serviceable at all, given that on one of the options recently explored, its explication of the notion of valid inference is inadequate. Classical statement logic (and predicate logic) remain serviceable so long as they are not applied to problematic cases, in particular to inferences in which the conjunction of premises is logically false or the conclusion is logically true. So long as the right sort of connection between the meanings of premises and conclusion is maintained, classical statement logic remains an extremely simple and reliable tool for evaluating the relevant class of inferences.

Given its potential inadequacies, we should not be led to draw the wrong conclusions from classical statement logic. For example, one frequently finds the claim, in the work of philosophers of science inspired by logic, that science rejects logically inconsistent theories because they have arbitrary consequences. To be sure, science does reject logically inconsistent theories, but not for the stated reason. While it is true that, given the rules of classical statement logic, inconsistent theories have arbitrary consequences, no physicist (nor any other reasonable person) would *infer* from the inconsistency of Niels Bohr's atomic theory either that the moon is made of green cheese (a factually false conclusion) or that the speed of light is a universal constant (a true conclusion, given the present state of knowledge). Such conclusions follow validly from Bohr's atomic theory on the rules of classical statement logic and should therefore, by those same rules, be compelling to anyone who believes in the theory. That they nonetheless fail to appeal at all should make us all the more suspicious of classical statement logic's inadequacy in this regard.

✱*Exercise 2.17.* Show (as economically as possible) that the following statements are tautologies:

1. $p→(q→p)$
2. $p→(q→p∧q)$
3. $p→(¬p→q)$
4. $p→((p→q)→q)$
5. $q→(p→p)$

Logician Wilhelm Ackermann has argued (in *Journal of Symbolic Logic* 21 [1956]: 113–28) that these formulas are *not* logical truths, if the arrow (→) is read as strict implication. Why?

2.5. Logical Equivalence

a. Definition

Our path toward the definition of the central notion of statement-logical equivalence will be familiar. We begin with an example.

Example 2.26. a. Susan doesn't drink, and she doesn't smoke.
  b. It is not the case that Susan drinks or smokes.

Clearly, both statements describe the same state of affairs, differing only in their formulations. However, from the point of view of statement logic, this is not simply one of those cases in which we encounter logically insignificant different colloquial expressions, such as the alternative turns of phrase with which we express one and the same truth-functional connective. There is a logical difference between the two formulations in Example 2.26 that becomes immediately clear on examination of the most fine-grained of their logical forms:

Example 2.26a. a. $¬p∧¬q$
  b. $¬(p∨q)$

But if a and b differ on the level of their logical forms, how is it possible that they nonetheless describe the same state of affairs? This puzzle may be resolved by comparing the truth tables for the two formulas: their main columns are identical (See Exercise 2.13). In other words, whenever a given interpretation makes 2.26a.a true (or false), it also makes 2.26a.b true (or false), and vice versa. Though the two logical forms are distinct, in both cases the constituent statements are so combined as to ensure that the resulting compound statements are always true or false under exactly the same conditions. This is to be expected, for if the two statements in 2.26 really do describe the same state of affairs, their truth values (as functions of the truth values of their constituent statements) cannot differ. The two logical forms in 2.26a are thus equivalent in the sense of providing different arrangements of constituent statements, which nonetheless assert the same thing. But the equivalence of the two statements in 2.26 is confined to the states of affairs they are used to describe; they are *not* equivalent in length or in stylistic quality. This is the kind of equivalence of statements, or statement forms, that will be targeted in our definition of *logical* equivalence. The precise import of this notion will be revealed over the course of the following section. Logical equivalence is easily defined by means of the biconditional. Biconditional statements are true whenever both of their constituent statements have the same truth value, and the same holds for the relation of logical equivalence. In stating the desired definition, we might follow the same procedure used in Definition 2.11, defining logical equivalence first for statements and then for statement forms, before uniting the two parts. But since the defining thrust of both partial definitions would be the same, we move directly to the concise version:

> *Definition 2.12.* Let *A* and *B* be statements or SL formulas. *A* and *B* are said to be statement-logically equivalent just in case $A \leftrightarrow B$ is a tautology.

We will use the symbol '≡' to represent the relation of logical equivalence, writing '$A \equiv B$' for "*A* and *B* are logically equivalent." Because logical equivalence depends on the tautology of the corresponding biconditional, we might also write '$\vDash (A \leftrightarrow B)$' or, without parentheses, '$\vDash A \leftrightarrow B$'.

Two remarks on this definition of statement-logical equivalence are immediately in order:

1. As before, when contrasting the conditional with the relation of validity, we should note that the biconditional and the relation of logical equivalence belong to different levels of language. The symbol '↔' stands for an object-language connective, while '≡' belongs to metalogic.

2. There are aspects of logical equivalence, which remind us of the so-called paradoxes of implication covered in section II.2.4.f; but, on closer inspection, the resemblance is superficial. It turns out that every logical truth is equivalent to every other (and every logical falsehood to every other), though at first blush they do not all appear to be saying the same thing. But we recall our observations in section II.2.2.a, in which we discovered that while logical truths are technically statements in the sense of Definition 1.1, they cannot be used to assert anything. It follows that they *are* all equivalent: they all assert nothing. It matters little whether we say, "This book is well-bound or it is not well-bound" or "The author of this book has taken great pains, or he has not taken great pains"; both sentences are completely vacuous. (This holds only if the sentences are read "straight," without any hidden meanings. Of course it is possible to imagine contexts in which either one might be used indirectly to convey some message. For example, the first might be used, indirectly, to draw attention to the binding of this book, while the second prompts us to consider the pains taken by its author.)

b. The Insertion Theorem

A good way to get clear on the meaning of logical equivalence is to contrast it with the *identity* relation for statements. Two statements are said to be identical if they have not one or several but *all* of their properties in common (as to what sorts of properties statements have in the first place, this depends on what we understand a statement to be; compare section I.4.1, Remark 4.). The logical equivalence of statements is weaker than the identity relation. Logically equivalent statements do not have all their properties in common; they are the same only from a *logical* perspective. Logically, the only respect in which they may differ is one we have already seen: pairs of logically equivalent statements often diverge in at least one of their logical forms. Otherwise, logically equivalent statements share the same logical properties and participate in the same logical relations: when one is logically true, so is the other; when one has a particular statement as a logical consequence, so does the other, and so on. This aspect of the relation of logical equivalence can be summed up in the following theorem for SL formulas:

> **The Insertion Theorem:** Let F_A be an SL formula containing A as a constituent formula. Let F_B be the formula that results from replacing one or more (though not necessarily all) occurrences of A in F_A with SL formula B. The theorem states that if $A \equiv B$, then $F_A \equiv F_B$.

Proof of the Insertion Theorem: What must be shown is that by the definition of logical equivalence, truth tables for F_A and F_B coincide in their main columns. Suppose, first, that both F_A and F_B contain the same number of sentential letters n, so that their truth tables both contain 2^n rows. Examine both truth tables at any arbitrary row. Since $A \equiv B$, and since the only respect in which F_A and F_B differ is that the latter contains B at one or more locations where A occurs in the former, it must be the case that in all columns where F_A and F_B differ, the same truth value appears. Therefore, the whole formulas F_A and F_B must also be assigned the same truth values.

Now suppose that F_A contains n sentential letters, and F_B contains k sentential letters, where $n \neq k$. Either $n > k$ or $n < k$. If $n > k$, it is possible to construct a truth table for F_B containing 2^n rows by duplicating every row of the standard truth table for F_B, which contains 2^k rows, 2^{n-k} times. This truth table may be compared with the standard truth table for F_A, as above, and by the same reasoning, it must be the case that in all columns where F_A and F_B differ, the same truth value appears. If $n < k$, we construct a truth table with 2^k rows for F_A and again perform the same comparison, achieving the same result. Since F_A and F_B are always assigned the same truth values, $F_A \equiv F_B$. QED.

The following corollary to the Insertion Theorem best demonstrates the significance of logical equivalence. It asserts that logically equivalent formulas have the same logical consequences.

> *Corollary 1:* For SL formulas A, B, and C, let $A \equiv B$ and $A \vDash C$. The corollary states that $B \vDash C$.

Proof of Corollary 1: We must show that $\vDash B \rightarrow C$. Let $F_A = A \rightarrow C$ and $F_B = B \rightarrow C$. Since F_A and F_B fulfill the terms of the Insertion Theorem, $F_A \equiv F_B$, thus $A \rightarrow C \equiv B \rightarrow C$. Since $\vDash A \rightarrow C$, $\vDash B \rightarrow C$. QED.

Similarly, logically equivalent formulas may always be inferred from the same sets of premises:

> *Corollary 2:* For SL formulas A, B, and C, let $A \equiv B$ and $C \vDash A$. The corollary states that $C \vDash B$.

Proof of Corollary 2: Exactly like the proof of Corollary 1, except that $F_A = C \rightarrow A$ and $F_B = C \rightarrow B$.

Insofar as we are interested only in the logical properties of, or logical relations among, statements or SL formulas (where such relations include valid inference), there is no need to distinguish between logically equivalent statements or logically equivalent formulas. This is why statement logic need not mark the distinction between a given statement A and the statement "It is true that A," as discussed in section II.1.1.f. There I argued that A and "It is true that A" are indeed different statements. But because they are logically equivalent, the difference between them is irrelevant to any inquiry conducted within the bounds of statement logic. Similarly, insofar as we remain within those same bounds, it is not mistaken to think of the extensional connectives as defined by their truth tables (again, compare section II.1.1.f). Any differences between connectives with the same truth tables are not the province of statement logic, and we are within our rights to abstract away from them. To be sure, this abstraction should not be undertaken without a clear understanding of the conditions under which it is both possible and advantageous. We have now attained this understanding, and later on, in chapter 4, we will engage in the aforementioned process of abstraction. This process will enable us to formulate statement logic extremely concisely as a branch of mathematics.

c. Important Statement-Logical Equivalences
Some of the following statement-logical equivalences have already been demonstrated in the exercises. Others may be shown easily. The rest follow immediately from the definition.

1. The Principle of Double Negation: $p \equiv \neg\neg p$
This principle asserts that a single negation is canceled by a second. In some languages, such as Latin, this logical principle is mirrored syntactically, and a second negation cancels the first. In others, such as French, repeated negations serve rather as intensifiers, as when singer Edith Piaf declares, to the delight of her fans, "Je ne regrette rien!" The same holds for certain dialect expressions in English, as in "I *ain't* got *no* money." Here the speaker clearly wishes to emphasize the denial of any imputations of wealth.

But the principle of double negation, which we are now in a position to actually *prove,* is not simply "discovered" as an interesting fact of logic. Our recognition of the principle is like finding an Easter egg we ourselves hid, for we implicitly built the principle in from the outset. We did this back in Definition 1.1, when we defined a statement as a sentence that is either true or false, and then later when we defined negation as a truth-functional connective. It should be recalled that Definition 1.1 was intended not as a factual claim about statements, but rather as a way of circumscribing the subject matter of classical statement logic (compare section I.4.1).

2. The Principles of Tautology: $p \equiv p \wedge p$ and $p \equiv p \vee p$

The traditional names of these principles, "principle of tautology for conjunction" and "principle of tautology for disjunction," are somewhat misleading, since by Definition 2.12, *every* logical equivalence between two statements is given by the tautologous status of the corresponding biconditional. Unfortunately, we have little control over traditional names.

3. The Commutative Laws: $p \wedge q \equiv q \wedge p$; $p \vee q \equiv q \vee p$; $p \leftrightarrow q \equiv q \leftrightarrow p$

In conjunctions, disjunctions, and biconditionals, the order of the two constituent statements is reversible. Such commutative laws are familiar from arithmetic: $a + b = b + a$, and $ab = ba$. Note that the colloquial English 'and' is *not* always commutative; indeed, it is frequently not even truth-functional (compare section II.1.1.a). Consider the difference between the following two examples:

> *Example 2.27.* Bill took some pills, and he became ill.

> *Example 2.28.* Bill became ill, and he took some pills.

Here the 'and' straightforwardly implies a temporal and causal ordering of the two events.

4. The Associative Laws: $(p \wedge q) \wedge r \equiv p \wedge (q \wedge r)$; $(p \vee q) \vee r \equiv p \vee (q \vee r)$

Again, the analogy to addition and multiplication in arithmetic is obvious. Associative laws allow us to omit parentheses for conjunctions with more than two conjuncts or for disjunctions with more than two disjuncts. We may write: $p \wedge q \wedge r$.

5. The Distributive Laws: $p \wedge (q \vee r) \equiv (p \wedge q) \vee (p \wedge r)$;
   $p \vee (q \wedge r) \equiv (p \vee q) \wedge (p \vee r)$

The distributive laws for conjunction and disjunction are similar. Distributive laws are familiar from algebra—for example, $a(b + c) = ab + ac$—but while multiplication distributes over addition, addition does not distribute over multiplication. Conjunction and disjunction both distribute over each other.

6. De Morgan's Laws: ¬(p∧q) ≡ ¬p∨¬q; ¬(p∨q) ≡ ¬p∧¬q

De Morgan was a nineteenth-century mathematician and logician. These laws were known to medieval logicians but forgotten in early modernity.

7. The Principle of Transposition: p→q ≡ ¬q→¬p

The principle of transposition has as an immediate consequence that whenever $A \models B$, $\neg B \models \neg A$. Intuitively, it is easy to see why. Suppose we know (1) that B is a logical consequence of A, and, further, (2) that $\neg B$ holds. Now we ask, can A hold? Clearly not, for if it did, then by (1) B would also hold. But by (2), we know $\neg B$. So $\neg A$ must hold.

It is depressing to discover how many arguments commit the fallacy of inferring from $A \models B$ that $\neg A \models \neg B$. This inference is invalid, because $p \rightarrow q$ is *not* equivalent to $\neg p \rightarrow \neg q$, as may be easily shown using truth tables or a simple example. If it is true that "It is raining→The street is wet," it need hardly be true that "It is not raining→The street is not wet." There is more than one way to soak a roadway.

8. The Elimination of Connectives

Up to now, our SL formulas have been replete with the connectives ∧, ∨, ¬, →, and ↔. But sometimes it is expedient, especially in mathematical treatments of statement logic, to make do with fewer connectives. The reduction is best accomplished not by simply prohibiting the use of a given connective but by showing how the logical properties of that connective might be expressed by means of others. The way to do this is with logical equivalences. For example, if we want to eliminate the biconditional, we need only appreciate the following equivalence:

$p \leftrightarrow q \equiv (p \rightarrow q) \wedge (q \rightarrow p)$

This equivalence has the added virtue of explaining why the biconditional is called "biconditional": it is a double conditional. Now, if we want to get rid of the conditional as well, we need only recall its original definition (see section II.1.1.d):

$p{\rightarrow}q \equiv \neg(p{\wedge}\neg q)$

The elimination of connectives typically results in longer formulas, but in compensation we get by with fewer symbols. This is sometimes a significant advantage in a mathematical treatment of logic. Such a treatment can be made especially concise if we use only the negation and conditional, in which case we would have to eliminate biconditional, disjunction, and conjunction. The biconditional has already been dealt with. Eliminating the disjunction and conjunction in favor of the conditional and negation is accomplished by means of the following equivalences:

$p{\vee}q \equiv \neg p{\rightarrow}q,$ and

$p{\wedge}q \equiv \neg(p{\rightarrow}\neg q)$

A system of connectives in which, with the help of logical equivalences, all of the other connectives may be captured is called a "functionally complete system of connectives." What would the smallest possible functionally complete system of connectives look like? How far can the elimination of connectives be taken? We turn to these questions now.

9. The Sheffer Stroke

In 1913, logician H. M. Sheffer discovered that all of the familiar truth-functional connectives could be captured by means of a single connective, the Sheffer Stroke or exclusion (Charles Sanders Peirce had made this same discovery several decades earlier but did not publish it at the time). The truth table for the exclusion is as follows:

A_1	A_2	$A_1 \mid A_2$
T	T	F
T	F	T
F	T	T
F	F	T

The following equivalences allow us to eliminate all of the other connectives in favor of the exclusion: $\neg p \equiv p \mid p$; $p \wedge q \equiv (p \mid q) \mid (p \mid q)$; $p \vee q \equiv (p \mid p) \mid (q \mid q)$; $p \rightarrow q \equiv p \mid (q \mid q)$; $p \leftrightarrow q \equiv (p \mid q) \mid ((p \mid p) \mid (q \mid q))$ (see Exercise 2.18).

Exercise 2.18. Prove the following:

1. $\neg p \equiv p \mid p$
2. $p \wedge q \equiv (p \mid q) \mid (p \mid q)$
3. $p \vee q \equiv (p \mid p) \mid (q \mid q)$
4. $p \rightarrow q \equiv p \mid (q \mid q)$
5. $p \leftrightarrow q \equiv (p \mid q) \mid ((p \mid p) \mid (q \mid q))$

How might the exclusion be rendered colloquially? What simple ways are there of capturing the exclusion by means of the other connectives?

10. Generalization by Means of the Substitution Theorem

The Substitution Theorem (section II.2.2.b) allows us to generalize all of the equivalences listed in points 1–9 above by replacing single sentential letters with SL formulas. For example, it is not only the case that $p \equiv \neg\neg p$; rather, $G \equiv \neg\neg G$ for any arbitrary SL formula G.

11. The Export-Import Law

The so-called export-import law, which often plays a role in mathematically oriented constructions of logic, consists of the following equivalence:

$p \wedge q \rightarrow r \equiv p \rightarrow (q \rightarrow r)$

A truth table for the corresponding biconditional will quickly persuade us of this equivalence. Now we recall the method of generalization, by means of the Substitution Theorem, described in point 10. We transform the above equivalence by substituting an arbitrary formula C in place of 'p', formula A in place of 'q', and formula B in place of 'r', yielding the following:

$$C{\land}A{\rightarrow}B \equiv C{\rightarrow}(A{\rightarrow}B)$$

This equivalence means that for arbitrary formulas A, B, and C, $C{\land}A{\rightarrow}B$ and $C{\rightarrow}(A{\rightarrow}B)$ always have the same truth values. It follows that whenever $C{\land}A{\rightarrow}B$ is logically true, so is $C{\rightarrow}(A{\rightarrow}B)$, and vice versa. In other words, $C{\land}A{\vDash}B$ just in case $C{\vDash}A{\rightarrow}B$. The abbreviation 'C' serves as a mnemonic for "condition" in the following reformulation: If it is the case that B follows from A under condition C, then it is also the case that the conditional $A{\rightarrow}B$ follows from condition C, and vice versa.

12. The Equivalence p→¬p ≡ ¬p

We are quickly persuaded of the validity of $p{\rightarrow}{\neg}p \equiv {\neg}p$ by the two-line truth table for $(p{\rightarrow}{\neg}p){\leftrightarrow}{\neg}p$. This equivalence allows us to shed new light on the so-called paradoxes of implication (section II.2.4.f.). Together with the Substitution Theorem (section II.2.2.b), the equivalence entails that for any statement or formula A, $A{\rightarrow}{\neg}A \equiv {\neg}A$. Let us suppose that $A{\rightarrow}{\neg}A$ is a logical truth. By definition of validity (section II.2.4.d), it follows from this supposition that ${\neg}A$ may be validly inferred from A; the truth of A guarantees the truth of ${\neg}A$! But this seems logically impossible. How might we approach this puzzle?

The key lies in the above equivalence itself. What it asserts is that positing that ${\neg}A$ follows from A, which is the same as positing the logical truth of $A{\rightarrow}{\neg}A$, is equivalent to positing the logical truth of ${\neg}A$, or the logical falsehood of A. By supposition, A is also the premise of the valid inference $A{\vDash}{\neg}A$. Our equivalence clears things up. What it tells us is that ${\neg}A$ follows validly from A just in case A is a logical falsehood. And this inference is made possible by shameless exploitation of Definition 2.11, on which *anything* may be validly inferred from contradictory premises, even ¬*A* from *A*.

Together with the Insertion Theorem, the equivalences cited in 1–10 (and others) are useful tools for the simplification of formulas. We may simplify a complex formula by finding a shorter formula with which it is logically equivalent. As an elementary example, consider the formula ¬(¬*p*∧¬*q*). By De Morgan's laws, this becomes ¬¬*p*∨¬¬*q*. Applying the principle of double negation, we obtain the considerably simpler formula *p*∨*q*. Such transformations are frequently written as chains of equivalences:

$$\neg(\neg p \wedge \neg q) \equiv \neg\neg p \vee \neg\neg q \equiv p \vee q$$

The technique of performing transformations of formulas by means of equivalences is less a matter of thought than mere mechanical calculation. There is no need to retain the meaning of a complex statement in one's head; all one has to do is manipulate strings of symbols in accordance with particular rules. As we will see later on, this patently mathematical aspect makes it possible to treat formal logic as a mathematical discipline (see chap. 4).

✳*Exercise 2.19.* Simplify the following formulas by means of appropriate logical equivalences:

　　1. ¬(¬*p*∨¬*q*)∨¬(¬*p*∨¬*r*)
　　2. ¬(¬*p*∨¬(*q*∨¬(¬*p*∨*q*)))
　　3. *p*→(*q*→(*p*∧*q*))

Which equivalences are most useful when we encounter tautologous or logically false disjuncts and conjuncts?

2.6. Logical Inconsistency

When it is said that two statements are inconsistent with one another, what is meant is that they are engaged in a certain kind of competition. It is a competition for the truth, for when one of two mutually inconsistent statements is true, the other cannot be, and vice versa. This is why telling someone that his or her statements are inconsistent is an *accusation*, because if they are, the accused *cannot* simultaneously make the same claim to truth on behalf of all of them. Note that inconsistency, in this sense, is a relation *between* statements and has nothing to do with the factual truth or falsehood of one or another of them. It is entirely possible for two false statements to be inconsistent with one another:

> *Example 2.29.*   A. New York is the capital of the United States.
> B. New York is the capital of Mexico.

There are two ways in which this somewhat vague notion of inconsistency, as a competition for the truth between two opposing statements, can be further refined.

One way is to consider the underlying cause of the conflict between two mutually inconsistent statements. Example 2.29 is a *conceptual* inconsistency: it is part of the concept "capital" that a given city can only be capital of one country; by contrast, it might be "sister city" to several other cities. But some inconsistencies arise on purely logical grounds, in which case we say that conflicting statements are *logically inconsistent*. What does it mean to call a given inconsistency *logical*? It means that the inconsistency arises in virtue of one or another logical form of the competing statements. Depending on the nature of the competing forms, we may wish to further specify. There are statement-logical inconsistencies between statements, on which we will have more to say shortly, and there are predicate-logical inconsistencies.

The second approach is to distinguish between a stronger and a weaker kind of inconsistency between statements. The word 'contradiction' will be reserved for the stronger sort of opposition, and two statements opposed to one another in this way will be called "contradictory." Two statements inconsistent with one another in the *weaker* way will be called "contrary." This distinction of a varying degree of mutual inconsistency is independent of the distinction that takes different causes of mutual inconsistency into account, considered in the preceding paragraph (in mathematical slang: the two distinctions are "orthogonal" to one another). There are thus statement-logical contraries and contradictions, as well as predicate-logical contraries and contradictions, as well as conceptual contraries and contradictions. We turn first to statement-logical contraries.

a. Statement-Logical Contraries

As stated above, contraries represent the weaker kind of mutual inconsistency. The basic idea is that two statements are said to be contrary to one another (as opposed to contradictory), if despite the fact that they cannot both be simultaneously true, it is nonetheless possible that they might both be *false*. Statement-logical contraries are pairs of statements that stand in this relation due to specific statement forms. Consider the following example:

> *Example 2.30.* A. Martin went to the city, and Martin went to the movies.
> B. Martin didn't go to the movies.

Clearly, the truth of A would rule out the truth of B, and vice versa. Still, it is possible for *both* statements to be false. There are other possibilities besides A and B. Martin might have gone to the movies in the country, in which case B is clearly false, and A is false because its first conjunct is false. It is natural to suppose, as in fact turns out to be the case, that the inconsistency of A with B derives from their having the statement forms $p \wedge q$ and $\neg q$, respectively. If it is impossible for A and B to both be true simultaneously, it must be impossible for their conjunction to be true. So when we consider the formula $(p \wedge q) \wedge \neg q$, we find it is indeed a logical falsehood (Exercise 2.14). Two statements A and B for which there are logical forms such that $A \wedge B$ is logically false can never be true simultaneously—though they might still both be false. Our definition of statement-logical contrariness is thus as follows:

> **Definition 2.13.** Let A and B be statements or SL formulas. A and B are said to be statement-logically contrary just in case $A \wedge B$ is a statement-logical falsehood.

b. Statement-Logical Contradictions

Statement-logical contradiction demands more than statement-logical contrariness; it is thus a stronger form of inconsistency. Like contraries, contradictory statements cannot both be true; but in addition, they cannot both be false. Put more succinctly, contradictory statements must always have opposing truth values. One must be the negation of the other.

> *Example 2.31.* A. The moon has risen.
>
> B. The moon has not risen.

Leaving aside the marginal case, in which the moon is just peeking over the horizon, there is no way for the two statements to be either simultaneously true or simultaneously false; their truth values are always diametrically opposed. Clearly, this is because B is the negation of A. The relationship between the two statements is easily articulated by means of the biconditional: the corresponding biconditional must always be false. Our definition reads:

> **Definition 2.14.** Let A and B be statements or SL formulas. A and B are said to be statement-logically contradictory just in case $A \leftrightarrow B$ is a statement-logical falsehood.

> *Exercise 2.20.* Using Definitions 2.13 and 2.14, show that any two statement-logically contradictory statements must also be statement-logically contrary.

2.7. Logical Consistency

Consistency is the complement of contrariness: two statements are mutually consistent if they are *not* in competition for the truth—if it is possible
for both to be true simultaneously. Once again, we are dealing with a *relation* between two statements, one which has nothing to do with the truth
or falsehood of either one. One false and one true statement might easily
be consistent with one another, as in the following example:

> *Example 2.32.* A. New York is the capital of Mexico.
> B. Paris is the capital of France.

The consistency of two statements means only that their claims to truth do
not stand in each other's way. It does not rule out our having other reasons
for rejecting one statement or the other, or even both. Just as we distinguished between conceptual and logical contradictions, so we may similarly differentiate the notion of consistency. For example, we might find
two statements to be consistent on the basis of a comparison of their statement forms. In this case, all we can say is that *at the level of abstraction of
statement forms,* there is nothing that stands in the way of both being true
(though they might still be *conceptually* incompatible; see below). The
two statements are thus neither statement-logically contradictory nor
statement-logically contrary (see Exercise 2.20). Consequently, statement-
logical consistency can be defined as simply the denial of statement-logical
contrariness (see Definition 2.13):

> *Definition 2.15.* Let *A* and *B* be statements or SL formulas. *A* and *B* are said to
> be statement-logically consistent just in case *A*∧*B* is not a logical falsehood.

If all we know about the relationship between two statements is that they
are statement-logically consistent, we really know very little. We know that
they are not in competition on statement-logical grounds, or on grounds
of their statement forms, but there are many other reasons why statements
can be mutually incompatible. For example, as far as statement logic is
concerned, the following two statements are absolutely consistent:

Example 2.33. A. No one can read this book in three days.

B. A diligent student can read this book in three days.

The two statements are statement-logically consistent because the most fine-grained statement form for their conjunction is $p \land q$, clearly not a statement-logical falsehood. The underlying inconsistency of A and B (which incidentally rests on the indisputable fact that there *are* diligent students) must thus be sought on a level that statement logic cannot address. How is this possible? Broadly speaking, the reason is that statement forms are the result of a process of abstraction, and inconsistency can often reside in something that does not survive this process. In the specific case of Example 2.33, the inconsistency derives from the fact that while the first statement asserts that "no one can," the second insists that "a diligent student can." But, in the move to statement forms, the meanings of "no one" and "a diligent student" are abstracted away, so that seen through the lens of statement logic, the two statements are consistent. Diagnosing this kind of inconsistency requires an analytic tool capable of sifting the components of atomic statements. The inconsistency of the two statements in Example 2.33 will come within our grasp only after we have developed predicate logic (see chap. 3). Still further inconsistencies cannot be captured by logic at all:

Example 2.34. A. Bill is a giant.

B. Bill is a dwarf.

The inconsistency of these two statements has nothing to do with their logical forms—and here it does not matter whether we are working within statement logic, predicate logic, or any other branch of logic. It rests instead on the meanings of the expressions employed in the statements. This is a *conceptual* (or *semantic)* inconsistency.

2.8. Logical Dependence

When we say that two statements are mutually dependent, we mean that the truth or falsity of one tells us something about the truth or falsity of the other. Such dependence can derive from a range of different sources. One possibility is that it rests on one or another logical form. In particular, the two statements, or their negations, may stand in a relation of logical consequence. So, A and B are logically dependent if, say, $A \vDash B$, $B \vDash A$, $A \vDash \neg B$, or $\neg B \vDash A$. Such relations permit us to infer the truth or falsehood of B from A, or the truth or falsity of A from B. Combinatorially, there are four additional possibilities, namely $\neg A \vDash B$, $B \vDash \neg A$, $\neg A \vDash \neg B$, and $\neg B \vDash \neg A$, but as each of these is equivalent with one of the previous logical consequences, they offer us no novel dependencies. $\neg A \vDash B$, for example, is equivalent to $\neg B \vDash A$, as shown by the following considerations:

$\neg A \vDash B$ means that $\neg A \rightarrow B$ is logically true.

$\neg B \vDash A$ means that $\neg B \rightarrow A$ is logically true.

But by the principles of transposition and double negation, $\neg A \rightarrow B$ and $\neg B \rightarrow A$ are logically equivalent: $\neg A \rightarrow B \equiv \neg B \rightarrow \neg\neg A \equiv \neg B \rightarrow A$. Logically equivalent statements always have the same truth value, and so the logical truth of one statement is inseparable from the logical truth of the other.

The following definition recommends itself:

Definition 2.16. Let A and B be statements or SL formulas. A and B are said to be statement-logically dependent just in case $A \vDash B$, $B \vDash A$, $A \vDash \neg B$, or $\neg B \vDash A$.

There are two important special cases of logical dependence.

Definition 2.17. Let A and B be statements or SL formulas. A is said to be statement-logically necessary for B just in case $B \vDash A$.

It should be emphasized that what is *necessary* for B are B's *consequences*! This is because something that is necessary for B is something that must always obtain whenever B does. So when A is necessary for B, this means that when B obtains, we may infer that A does, too. The reciprocal dependence, which allows us to infer that B obtains from the fact that A obtains, is named in the following definition:

Definition 2.18. Let *A* and *B* be statements or SL formulas. *A* is said to be statement-logically sufficient for *B* just in case *A*⊨*B*.

The failure to respect the distinction between necessary and sufficient conditions, or to recognize the distinction in the first place, is one of the most common argumentative errors. Sometimes necessity and sufficiency are combined in a single condition, both necessary and sufficient. It can be shown that *A* is both necessary and sufficient for *B* just in case *A* ≡ *B* (Exercise 2.21).

✳*Exercise 2.21*
    1. Show that *A* is necessary and sufficient for *B* just in case *A* ≡ *B*.
    2. Show that two SL formulas that are either logically equivalent, or contrary, or contradictory, must be logically dependent.

3. Review and Overview

3.1. Review

How far have we gotten in statement logic? We began by identifying extensional connectives (such as the conditional) at the level of statements, the object-level. Next we introduced the concept of statement form, tailor-made for these connectives, followed by the corresponding concept of extensional interpretation. Moving to the metalevel, we first explicated the notions of statement-logical truth and statement-logical falsehood, making essential use of extensional interpretation in the process. The definitions of subsequent metalogical notions all depended on that of logical truth, making this concept fundamental to metalogic. In discussing valid inference we encountered a complication, which we traced to the extensional character of the conditional, on which the definition of validity depends. We made progress toward understanding the complication but were unable to resolve it completely. Additional metalogical notions were defined without further difficulties, always by means of the notion of statement-logical truth.

I would like to conclude with three general remarks on statement logic. First, I return to a problem first raised in section I.4.1, the problem of understanding the nature of statements themselves or, in other words, the problem of determining what statement logic is actually about (3.2). Next, I ask whether, and in what sense, logic provides a justification for valid inference (3.3). This discussion will allow us to address, to some degree, the question of whether the development of logic inevitably involves a circular relationship between object-level and metalevel (3.4).

3.2. Statements and Statement Logic

In statement logic, the compelling appeal of valid inferences can be traced to the repeated occurrence of extensionally connected constituent statements. This assessment, however, has been based entirely on our reading of examples and has not otherwise been justified (see section II.2.4.b, Criterion 1). But it is possible to actually prove that no SL formula can be logically true unless it contains at least one statement letter that occurs more than once (provided we assume that such formulas include no connectives for which the truth tables contain only Ts or only Fs). This proof may be found in appendix 1. In other words, statement-logical truths and statement-logically valid inferences must contain at least one repeated constituent statement. But this fact is of some importance to the question first raised in section I.4.1: What *is* a statement, for purposes of statement logic? For talk of repeated constituent statements to make any sense at all, statements must be the sort of things that are capable of repeated occurrence in the first place. It follows that statement logic cannot make do with an understanding of statements as singular physical events, such as particular concrete utterances (which consist of strings of sounds produced at a particular place and spanning a particular temporal interval), or actual inscriptions. Such events are necessarily historically unique and thus unrepeatable. The conception of statements appropriate to statement logic must therefore designate something more abstract, something susceptible to repetition. The repeated constituent statements occurring in an inference might be understood, for example, as different instantiations of one and the same statement template. What this suggestion does not tell us is how such templates should be understood in turn—perhaps as inscription templates, assertion templates, or judgment templates. Another possibility would be to understand a statement as consisting in its meaning: in the particular state of affairs (whatever that might be) described by the concrete utterance or inscription. The *meanings* of concrete utterances and inscriptions *can* be repeatedly uttered or inscribed.

Once again, I must beg off any further consideration of these proposals for how best to understand the sense of "statement" appropriate to statement logic. But our discussion so far has yielded the interesting insight that, by virtue of its subject matter, logic must from the outset operate on an abstracted plane, abstracted relative to the concrete physical affairs of the world. For purposes of statement logic, statements cannot be any sort of concrete physical event or condition, for the latter are always historically unique and unrepeatable. Furthermore, it is worth noting that this insight into the subject matter of statement logic emerges out of the formal apparatus of statement logic itself and is not the result of any reflections imported from outside logic proper.

3.3. Does Logic Justify Valid Inference?

Logic was once often described as the study of sound thinking. This characterization has since fallen largely into disfavor, as it can easily lead to misunderstanding logic as a discipline of mental hygiene. Contemporary logic has completely stifled these psychological overtones (though very widespread, especially in the nineteenth century, such views were convincingly refuted by Frege and Husserl). Nowadays logic is more frequently characterized as the study of valid inference or logical consequence. Though there is nothing wrong with this description, it does raise certain problems. Of course statement logic is concerned with the distinction between valid and invalid inferences. However, this distinction is not supposed to be arbitrary, but rather justified. The decision to classify a given inference as valid cannot be made whimsically; it must come as the result of compelling argument. In other words, in logic we cannot be content with a mere *description* of valid inferences, not even a complete listing of them; we must also be able to *justify* the judgment that some inferences, and not others, are valid. And from what we have learned, logic appears to accomplish this task admirably: it allows us, at least in the absence of linguistic ambiguity, to establish the validity of a given inference beyond the shadow of a doubt. Here "beyond the shadow of a doubt" means that filling in the truth table for the appropriate formula (the formula for an SF of "Conjunction of premises→conclusion") provides a mathematical proof of the validity (or invalidity) of the inference in question. And the human mind can hardly ask for greater cognitive certainty than that furnished by mathematical proof—or so twenty-five hundred years of mathematical, scientific, and philosophical history teach us. So statement logic not only *describes* valid inferences, it also provides us with *indisputable justification* of their validity. Where's the problem?

The problems begin to become evident once we ask what proofs actually are. Proofs are inferences from particular premises. The proof of a given claim always operates under the assumption that the relevant premises are true and the inferences valid. What are the premises for a proof that one or another form of inference is valid or invalid? In this case, the most important premise is the definition of valid inference, Definition 2.11, which sets the standard for statement-logical validity: if a given inference satisfies the definition, it is valid; otherwise, it is invalid, at least in statement logic. How was Definition 2.11 justified? First we recall that this definition really was justified, because the very nature of Definition 2.11 demanded it. Definition 2.11 is an explication, not a more or less arbitrary synthetic definition (see section II.2.4.a). Our justification proceeded by reflection on adequacy criteria, where Definition 2.11 emerged ineluctably out of Criteria 1–4 (see section II.2.4.d). But how were the adequacy criteria justified? They were made plausible by reflection on a few examples of inferences, in particular Example 2.19, which we assumed to be valid:

Fred was drunk or on drugs. Fred was not drunk. Therefore, Fred was on drugs. But this inference was *assumed* to be valid; its validity was taken for granted. The assumed validity of this example was the whole basis for our formulation of the adequacy criteria, which in turn served as the basis for Definition 2.11. In other words, our argument for the account of valid inference in Definition 2.11 ultimately rested on a small number of examples, whose validity (or invalidity, in the case of Example 2.21) was taken for granted from the outset. Indeed, it is hard to see how the four adequacy criteria could be made plausible without a certain familiarity with the phenomenon of valid inference—without some knowledge of valid and invalid inferences. It is no coincidence, and certainly no mere didactic trick, that logic textbooks so often begin with examples of valid and invalid inferences. These examples are the irreducible justificatory basis of logic itself. Under these circumstances, it would be absurd to claim that any application of Definition 2.11 could provide a *proof* of the validity of Example 2.11 (section II.2.4.d). Applying the definition to this example only shows that we have not made any grievous errors in extracting the definition from the example. The criteria for valid inference were derived from Example 2.19, so it is no great surprise to find that they successfully apply to this case. The successful application of Definition 2.11 to Example 2.19 does not make the assumed validity of the latter one iota more certain. The validity of this example has not been justified.

How, then, should we describe the relationship between Definition 2.11 and particular inferences or inference forms? It would clearly be inaccurate to characterize it as a justificatory relationship running in only one direction. For it would be wrong to claim that all valid inference forms were justified by Definition 2.11, since some of them played a role in justifying the definition itself. On the other hand, Definition 2.11, for its part, does have a role to play in evaluating inferences: it can be used, for example, to draw our attention to seductive fallacies. The relationship between Definition 2.11 and particular inferences is thus a matter of what American philosopher John Rawls (1921–2002) aptly called "reflective equilibrium." A general definition of valid inference is formulated in light of specific examples of valid inference and then applied, in turn, to further examples. Such application has three possible outcomes. For inferences on whose validity we have no prior opinion, the definition provides us with an evaluation. For inferences on which we do have prior opinions, the definition may confirm our views, necessitating no further theoretical work. On the other hand, an application of the definition may disagree with our prior opinions. In this case, there are two possibilities: either our prior opinions are in error, or the definition itself is inadequate. We have no way of deciding in advance which of these two possibilities holds. When such disagreements are discovered, they are often the subject of long-standing dissent. The process of theory construction is only complete when our opinions on particular examples agree, possibly after correction, with the general definition—when our assumptions all cohere. Only then do we say that reflective equilibrium (between our general definition and particular applications) has been attained. This is precisely the process pursued in sections II.2.4.b through II.2.4.f. As for residual discrepancies between definition and example, these remain the focal point of real dissent among logicians. Such dissent continues to rage around the so-called paradoxes of implication (section II.2.4.f).

3.4. On the Relationship between Object-Level, and Metalevel in Logic

There is one further reason why talk of formal logic as providing proofs or justifications for inference forms remains extremely problematic. In the previous section, I asserted that proofs of the validity of particular inferences must always start from certain premises. I also explored one important premise of such proofs in detail. But in addition to their premises, proofs also rely on certain inferences. These are the subject of the present section. The problem is as follows. Logic is often described as the study of valid arguments. This is not quite right, since there are valid inferences that fail to constitute *arguments* for their conclusions—for example, $A \vDash A$. But still, it is reasonable to suppose that logic makes a significant contribution to the foundations of argumentation. If this is the case, we discover a peculiar circular structure emerging within logic. On the one hand, throughout this introduction to logic I have made every effort to justify every step, every new distinction, by means of argument. On the other hand, this same logic is supposed to provide a foundation for argumentation itself. But how can this be if the very development of logic takes valid argumentation for granted?

This difficulty becomes particularly pointed when we consider the "proofs" of the validity of particular inference forms (I have placed scare quotes around "proofs" because, as shown in the previous section, their status as actual proofs is problematic). In order to perform such a proof, we must not only assume certain premises, we must also use certain rules of inference. The proof, in turn, is meant to establish the validity of just such inference rules. This does not automatically lead to circularity, since the inference rules *used* in a given proof need not be the same as those *established* by the proof. But the circularity becomes unavoidable when we ask after the validity of the inference rules used in the proofs themselves. If we attempt to *prove* their validity, using what we are trying to prove in the process, the resulting proof will be circular and thus unpersuasive. If instead we *give up* on trying to prove the rules of inference used in logic, then these rules rest on nothing. If there is no way of justifying the rules of inference used in the proofs of logic, the status of these proofs is equally dubious.

Many logic texts simply sweep this problem under the rug. In others it is dealt with as follows. In logic, we must strictly observe the distinction between the logic we are studying—in this chapter, statement logic—and the logic with which we conduct the study. Terminologically, this distinction is marked by the contrast between "object-logic" and "observer logic," respectively. This distinction separates an object-level from a corresponding metalevel; a similar separation occurs within statement logic itself (see section II.2.1). There is nothing wrong with this distinction, but it is important to note that by itself it cannot completely dispel the present problem. This failure will be shown by means of a particularly dramatic example.

Earlier, we defined the notion of statement-logical equivalence between two formulas or statements A and B by reference to the tautology of the corresponding biconditional $A \leftrightarrow B$ (section II.2.5.a). I now claim that A and B are statement-logically equivalent, just in case $A \vDash B$ and $B \vDash A$. This claim demands a proof. A proof of a claim of the form "X just in case Y" is performed by showing that X is a logical consequence of Y, and Y a logical consequence of X (in the present case, this would mean showing, by means of truth tables, first, that both $A \vDash B$ and $B \vDash A$ can be inferred from $A \equiv B$, and, second, that $A \equiv B$ can be inferred from $A \vDash B$ together with $B \vDash A$). But such a proof would make use, in observer logic, of the very same equivalence relation we are trying to establish for object-logic. Of course it is true that while the equivalence relation in observer logic is being *used,* the corresponding relation in object-logic is the *object of investigation.* But why bother proving the object-logic equivalence when we are already prepared to trust the validity of its observer logic counterpart? After all, either the equivalence holds in *both* object-logic and observer logic or it *fails* to hold in both. Just as before (see section II.3.3), when we questioned whether the validity of Example 2.19 could be tested by means of Definition 2.11 (where the example had motivated the definition in the first place), so we must ask, once again, whether we are really dealing with a proof.

As it turns out, however, the circularity is not quite so dire in the present case as it was for the proposed evaluation of Example 2.19. In that case, the "proof" in no way increased our confidence in the inference's validity. For present purposes, we should recognize that using a rule in observer logic does not imply that there is a proof for that same rule in object-logic. Only in this case would a circularity arise, making nonsense of our proofs. Consider the following example. Suppose we believe that $A \equiv B$ just in case $B \vDash A$. By "we believe," I mean that we simply use the claim in observer logic but require a proof of the corresponding claim in object-logic. Well, now to the proof! The "just in case" implies an equivalence, so in our proof of the claim for object-logic, we use the same claim in observer logic. We must then show that $A \equiv B$ is a logical consequence of $B \vDash A$. But this claim cannot be proved, for it is false. Presumably, this discovery would lead us to reflect on the alleged equivalence in observer logic, where we would likely abandon it.

When we question the real persuasiveness of our proofs of object-logical claims, it is difficult to entirely dispel our unease regarding the precise relationship between object-logic and observer logic. A first step toward easing our fears is to recognize that our use of inference rules in proofs is analogous to our assumption that certain examples constitute valid inferences, as discussed in the preceding section. Proofs do not come for free, and the proofs of inference rules are no exception. Realistically, we cannot expect to be able to develop and justify logic without making use of any assumptions. It is thus inevitable that certain inference rules be taken for granted in observer logic, or object-logic could never even get started. At best, the relationship between the inference rules of observer logic and those of object-logic will reach a reflective equilibrium. When it does, the arrow of justification will no longer point in only one direction. As the above example makes clear, we might well end up correcting observer logic from the perspective of object-logic, even though the latter could not have gotten started without the former. To be sure, the attainment of a reflective equilibrium between object-logic and observer logic would require that we first have a clear understanding of the tools of observer logic. At present, we have no such understanding, for we have never properly taken stock of these tools, though we continue to use them. We might in principle make up for our neglect, but not without untold complications. We would have to reexamine every argument given so far, decomposing and investigating all of its constituent parts. Instead, what we will do is develop, in chapter 4, a mathematical approach to statement logic, one in which the tools of observer logic are explicitly acknowledged from the outset.

3 ✳ Predicate Logic

We ought to begin by asking what remains, if anything, for an introduction to logic to accomplish now that our discussion of statement logic has been concluded. After all, the problems originally formulated in the introduction to this volume have been addressed, and the most important metalogical concepts explained, especially the notion of valid inference. But a motive for taking formal logic further appears immediately when we recall our very first example from section I.1:

> **Example 3.1.** All logicians are human.
> All humans need sleep.
> ✳
> Therefore, All logicians need sleep.

In our introductory chapter, this prototype valid inference served as our point of entry into logic. But when we attempt to test its validity by means of statement logic, we are severely disappointed. The premises and conclusion of Example 3.1 do not contain any truth-functional connectives, so the most fine-grained SF for the conjunction of premises is simply $p \wedge q$, while the most fine-grained SF for the conclusion is r. The validity of this inference would thus demand that $p \wedge q \rightarrow r$ be a tautology, which it is not. Clearly, then, the decisive logical characteristics of 3.1, the features that make the inference valid, are not captured by its statement forms. Indeed, the validity of 3.1 does not turn on the occurrence of extensional connectives and repeated constituent statements, as do statement-logically valid inferences. Instead, as we saw in the introduction, the mechanism of this inference relies on the occurrence of certain words, like 'all' and 'some', and on the repeated occurrence of other expressions (whose specific meanings do not matter). We also saw that the appeal of the inference is not in the slightest diminished if we replace 'logician', 'human', and 'need sleep' by letters:

Example 3.2.   All *A*s are *B*s.

All *B*s are *C*s.

*

Therefore,   All *A*s are *C*s.

On the other hand, replacing only *one* occurrence of the repeated expressions would be fatal to the validity of 3.1. Suppose, for example, we replace the second 'human' with 'recruits':

Example 3.3.   All logicians are human.

All recruits need sleep.

*

Therefore,   All logicians need sleep.

The validity of such examples as 3.1 and 3.2 evidently depends not only on such words as 'all' and 'some', but on the repeated occurrence of other expressions. The analysis of such inferences thus requires a notion of logical form that targets just the elements relevant to their validity, abstracting everything else away. This notion of logical form will be called "predicate form," for reasons which will soon become clear. Our construction of predicate logic will be analogous to that of statement logic, for the underlying line of argument is essentially the same. The role previously played by the connectives will now be played largely by such words as 'all', and the role of repeated constituent statements will now be played by repeated constituent concepts (compare section II.2.2.a, Remark 3; section II.2.4.b, Criterion 1; and section II.3.2). Along the way, however, we *will* discover some significant differences between statement and predicate logic.

1. The Symbol System of Predicate Logic

1.1. The Classification of Statements

We begin by restricting ourselves to statements containing no extensional or intensional connectives, the statements previously called "primitive" or "atomic" (section I.4.2). We will divide these primitive statements into three kinds, according to what has been called their "quantity." Provisionally, the quantity of a statement has to do with the number of objects with which the statement is concerned. Specifically, a statement can concern itself with a single, particular object, or with the existence of at least one object having specific characteristics, or with all of the objects in a given domain. This threefold distinction does not exhaust all of the possible quantities of objects with which a statement might be concerned, but, for reasons that will only be clear later on, it will suffice.

The distinction between the three quantities of statements is, in the following sense, analogous to statement logic's distinction between different truth-functional connectives (compare section II.1.1). The validity of statement-logically valid inferences turns on the meanings of connectives, and on the repeated occurrence of constituent statements. This is why we distinguished the various connectives, characterizing each by means of its truth table. Similarly, we distinguish the various quantities of statements because they turn out to contribute to the validity of predicate-logical inferences.

a. Singular Statements

Here is yet another example:

Example 3.4.   Socrates is a man.

This statement is *about something,* namely Socrates. In logic, we call this the "logical subject" of the statement:

> *Definition 3.1.* The logical subject of a statement is what the statement is about.

The word 'subject' has had a long and tumultuous history in philosophy. Its Latin root means, literally, "that which underlies." The turbulent history of the term 'subject' may doubtless be traced to the fact that, in a given situation, there may be widely diverging opinions on what it is that underlies—on what is fundamental. Regardless, the logical subject underlies its statement in the sense that, before anything can be asserted, it must first be determined what the assertion is to be about. In *singular statements,* the logical subject is a *single object,* an *individual.* The expressions "single object" and "individual" must, of course, be understood in a sense much broader than that familiar from colloquial usage. An "object" is ordinarily understood as some physical thing, while an "individual" is normally an individual human being. In predicate logic, however, the two expressions are used synonymously, in a broad sense, to refer to *any discrete unit* (including physical things and life forms, but also states of affairs, ideas, processes, etc.).

> *Definition 3.2.* In predicate logic, an individual or object can be any discrete unit.

In this sense, then, democracy, the number 17, God, the idea of freedom, my headache, the slow collapse of the Acropolis, my neighbor, and the set of all finite sets are all individuals or objects. The names of individuals are designated as follows:

> *Definition 3.3.* Words referring to individuals are called "individual names" or "individual constants."

(The expression "individual constant" will become intelligible only later.) In Example 3.4, 'Socrates' is thus an individual name, and Socrates himself, the logical subject of the statement, is an individual in the sense of Definition 3.2.

In Example 3.4, something is ascribed to the logical subject, Socrates, namely the attribute of being a man. In the negated statement "Socrates is not an animal," an attribute is denied of Socrates, namely that of being an animal. That which a statement ascribes to or denies of its logical subject is designated as follows:

> *Definition 3.4.* That which a statement ascribes to or denies of its logical subject is called the "logical predicate" of the statement.

The term "predicate" comes from the Latin "praedicere," meaning "to ascribe."

In logic, the notion of a logical predicate actually has much broader applicability than has yet been revealed. Up to now, the expression "logical predicate" looks like little more than a fancy way of saying "property." However, the notion also encompasses *relations,* which, rather than being ascribed *to* particular individuals, are said to hold *between* two or more. Consider the following example:

> *Example 3.5.*   Lake Michigan lies between the Atlantic and the Pacific.

This example asserts a specific geographical relation between three individuals, Lake Michigan, the Atlantic, and the Pacific. Taken together, Lake Michigan, the Atlantic, and the Pacific form the logical subject of 3.5, where the order in which the three occur is significant. A set of three objects in which the order matters in this way is called a *triple,* and an ordered set of n objects is called an "n-tupel." Such n-tupels are commonly represented by listing the names of their constituent objects in the correct order within round braces. The logical subject of 3.5 is thus the triple '(Lake Michigan, the Atlantic, the Pacific)'. The logical predicate ascribed to this logical subject is '. . . lies between . . . and . . .'. Predicates may be classified as follows according to the number of individuals to which they must be applied:

Definition 3.5. Predicates ascribed to logical subjects consisting of a single individual are called "one-place predicates"; the rest are called "*n*-place predicates" or "relations," where *n* is the number of individuals in the logical subjects to which these predicates are ascribed.

The predicate of Example 3.4, '. . . is a man', is thus a one-place predicate, while '. . . lies between . . . and . . .' is a three-place predicate.

One further device allows us to simplify our representation of predicates. Instead of using the ellipsis, '. . .' as a placeholder for individual names, as in '. . . is a man', we may use such letters as '*x*', as in "*x* is a man." Such placeholders need not always occur at the beginning; "Anthony hates *x*" is also a predicate, one which ascribes to some individual *x* (whatever that might be) the property of being hated by Anthony. For *n*-place predicates, we use *n* placeholders. The geographical relation cited in Example 3.5 can thus be rendered, "*x* lies between *y* and *z*."

✳Exercise 3.1. For the following sentences, identify the logical subject and predicate. How many places does the logical predicate have? (For some sentences, there is more than one correct answer.)

1. Veronica is sitting at the table.
2. Veronica and Stephen are sitting at the table.
3. Veronica is sitting across from Stephen.
4. Chicago is on Lake Michigan.
5. There are three bathers on the beach.
6. Lecturer *S* ordinarily begins her lectures promptly.
7. A bird in the hand is better than two in the bush.
8. Two birds in the hand are better than two birds in the bush.
9. It is raining.
10. Someone is sitting at the table.
11. Nobody is sitting at the table.

The concepts introduced above call for a number of further remarks.

1. Our discussion of singular statements has drawn our attention to an

apparently central feature of language and thought in general: the *predicative structure* of statements. It appears that what all thoughts and utterances have in common is that they are about something (the logical subject), to which they attribute (or of which they deny) something (the logical predicate). Several questions arise at this point. First, we must ask whether this predicative structure is primarily a feature of thought *or* of speech or language. If the latter, then it must also be asked whether all languages have predicative structure, or perhaps only Indo-European languages, of which English is one. On the other hand, if predicative structure is a feature of thought itself, how universal is it? Is it restricted to particular cultures, does it pertain to the entire human species, or is it perhaps a necessary characteristic of any possible process that deserves to be called "thought" in the first place? Perhaps it is more restricted even than any of these alternatives would seem to allow, since our own cultural realm also contains nonpredicative thought, hidden by virtue of the fact that it cannot be captured in statements. There might even be a kind of prepredicative thought, a precursor to predicative thought. Clearly, these questions would take us far beyond the bounds of logic, though it is logic that reveals them—provided we allow ourselves to probe its foundations.

2. Though the identification of a statement's logical subject and predicate is sometimes unequivocal, it need not be. It is unequivocal in Example 3.4, "Socrates is a man"; Socrates is the only possible logical subject, and "x is a man" is the only logical predicate. But consider Example 3.5: "Lake Michigan lies between the Atlantic and the Pacific." This statement might be understood as having Lake Michigan as its logical subject, to which it ascribes the one-place predicate, "x lies between the Atlantic and the Pacific." Alternatively, we might construe the pair (Lake Michigan, Pacific) as the logical subject, ascribing to it the two-place predicate, "x lies between the Atlantic and y." From the fact that many statements permit different alternative identifications of logical subject and predicate, it follows that, in general, a given statement cannot be said to have one definitive predicate form. Here, too, we see a direct parallel to statement logic,

in which a given statement frequently has more than one statement form (compare section II.1.2.b, Point 6)

3. "Logical subject" and "logical predicate" designate particular roles expressions can play within statements. Collectively, we will refer to them as the "logical role" of an expression, a notion to which we will return in explicating the predicate logic conception of valid inference. Because of the peculiarly logical perspective implicit in the notion of logical role, the distinction between logical subject and predicate fails to coincide with the similar distinction between grammatical subject and predicate. Example 3.5 makes this perfectly clear. In "Lake Michigan lies between the Atlantic and the Pacific," the grammatical subject is 'Lake Michigan', the grammatical predicate is 'lies', and 'between the Atlantic and the Pacific' is an adverbial phrase. The distinction between logical subject and predicate also fails to coincide with any grammatical distinctions among the parts of speech.

4. One and the same word can often be used to express predicates of differing numbers of places. In Example 3.5, the word "lies" expresses a three-place predicate (at least on one way of analyzing this statement). But this word can also be used to articulate a one-place predicate, as in 'The dog lies'.

5. The history of logic distinguishes so-called "classical logic" from "modern" or "mathematical logic." The latter name derives from the fact that, since the middle of the nineteenth century, this logic has evolved in concert with the treatment of problems in the foundations of mathematics. One of the many differences between classical and mathematical logic concerns their conceptions of the logical predicate. For *classical* logic, which divides all elementary statements into three parts, the logical predicate of a statement is a particular concept. In the example "Socrates is a man," 'Socrates' is the subject, '(a) man' is the predicate, and the word 'is' serves as the copula, the element that unites subject and predicate. In classical logic, all singular statements thus have the form "S is P." By contrast, *modern* logic distinguishes only the logical subject and logical predicate of singular statements. In our present example, 'Socrates' remains the

subject, but the predicate is the entire remainder of the sentence, "[place-holder] is a man." As to why modern logic imposed this change in the conception of the logical predicate, a proper discussion of this question would take us too far afield.

6. A slight simplification of our language is in order. Because in the context of predicate logic we are interested only in *logical* subject and predicate and not in the similarly named grammatical notions, we will henceforth allow ourselves to omit the adjective 'logical'.

7. To conclude this section, let us consider the definitions of two further concepts of importance to predicate logic:

Definition 3.6.
1. The *intension* of a predicate is the sense (or meaning) of the predicate.
2. The *extension* of a predicate is the set of objects to which the predicate applies.

For example, the intension of the predicate "x is red" is the property of redness, while the extension of this predicate is the set of all things to which the predicate applies, or the set of all red things. Matters are a bit more complicated for multiplace predicates, such as "x lies between y and z." The intension of this three-place predicate is the spatial relation of lying between, but what about its extension? The predicate is always ascribed to a particular triple—in our example, "(Lake Michigan, Atlantic, Pacific)." And, of course, there are many other triples to which the same predicate applies. The extension is thus the set of all such triples. In general, the extension of an n-place predicate is a set of n-tupels—a set of ordered sets of n elements.

There appears to be the following relation between intension and extension: the intension of a given predicate determines its extension, for the meaning of a predicate determines which set of objects the predicate applies to. In the case of "x is red," the property of redness applies to members of the set of red objects, making this set the predicate's extension. (It should be noted, however, that in the contemporary philosophy of language, it has been argued that intension fails to determine extension. For our purposes, such arguments need not concern us.) But the inverse relation does *not* hold: extension does not determine intension, because predicates with the *same* extension can have *different* intensions. One classic example is provided by the predicates "*x* is equilateral" and "*x* is equiangular," as applied to triangles. Both predicates have the same extension, since all equilateral triangles are also equiangular and vice versa. But the intensions of the two predicates are different, as they address different properties of triangles: being equilateral is not the same thing as being equiangular, even when the two properties are always correlated in triangles. The distinction between intension and extension is further illustrated by the perennial debate over whether the glass is half full or half empty. Extensionally speaking, there is no disagreement, since all half-full glasses are also half empty, and vice versa. Intensionally speaking, however, there is indeed a difference, one which sometimes, under the right conditions, serves as a source of endless discussion.

For the present, we will have to be content with simply noting that predicate intension is a highly problematic notion, just as problematic as the notion of a statement (compare section I.4.1). Once we start asking what the meaning of a predicate actually is, what it consists in, how it relates to how the predicate is used, etc., we enter an extremely contentious area of philosophical discussion. But this problem, like those surrounding the status of statements, is of relatively minor concern to formal logic, in the sense that such problems pose no obstacle to our further pursuit of predicate logic.

b. Universal Statements

The following is an example of a universal statement:

Example 3.6. All readers of this book are bored.

As was made clear in the introduction, the 'all' in this statement is logically significant, in the sense that it affects the validity or invalidity of inferences drawn from this statement. This word will thus belong to the predicate form of the statement and not to its content, where the content may be abstracted away in discussions of validity. First, however, we ought to consider what Example 3.6 is actually about. There are two possibilities: the statement might be about the set of the readers of this book as a collective whole, or it might be about all of the individual members of this set. Clearly it is the latter, for only individuals are capable of feeling boredom, not sets. (Of course matters are different in such statements as "The set of Snow White's dwarves has seven elements." This statement really is about the set as a whole, for the property of having seven elements applies to the set, not to its elements.) It follows that the predication in Example 3.6 applies to individuals, with the 'all' ensuring that *every one* of these individual readers is targeted.

In predicate logic we have a special way of transcribing universal statements like Example 3.6, one that employs a symbol analogous to those used in rendering the connectives of statement logic. This device will be particularly useful later on in the representation of predicate forms. It involves the use of the so-called universal quantifier, together with a corresponding *domain* or *universe of discourse*. Using the symbol '$\wedge$' for the universal quantifier, we may rewrite Example 3.6 as follows:

> **Example 3.6a.** $\wedge x$ (x is bored)
> Domain: the readers of this book

The universal quantifier, '$\wedge x$', is read, "for all x . . . ." Another symbol commonly used for this purpose is '$\forall$' (an upside-down 'A', for 'all'), and sometimes "for all x . . ." is written by simply placing the 'x' within round braces: '(x)'. The domain specification tells us to which individuals the 'all' applies, in this case all the readers of this book, and not, say, all long-haired dachshunds. Our symbol for the universal quantifier bears a suspicious resemblance to the symbol for conjunction. There is indeed a connection, for, after all, 3.6a asserts nothing more than the following:

Example 3.6b. Reader$_1$ is bored $\wedge$ reader$_2$ is bored $\wedge$ reader$_3$ is bored $\wedge \ldots$

In 3.6a and 3.6b it is quite clear to what subject the predicate is meant to apply: it is meant to apply to every individual reader x of this book. The variable 'x', as it occurs in Example 3.6a, has a special name:

> *Definition 3.7.* A variable to which a quantifier refers, and which ranges over a particular domain of individuals, is called a "bound individual variable" and is said to be bound by the quantifier.

'x' is called an "individual variable" because, rather than designating one fixed individual, it ranges over an entire domain. The variable is called "bound" because the quantifier which binds it determines *how* it varies over its domain.

> *Exercise 3.2. Rewrite the following statements using universal quantifiers and appropriate domains (some may have more than one correct transcription):
>
> 1. All bridges are pretty.
> 2. All long bridges are pretty.
> 3. All people love Fred.
> 4. Fred loves all people.
> 5. Every person loves Fred.
> 6. At that time everyone was unhappy.
> 7. All points on the circumference of a circle are equidistant from the center.

c. Existential Statements

Members of the third class of primitive statements are called "existential statements," also traditionally known as "particular statements."

> *Example 3.7.* There is at least one big-city dweller with lung disease.

In representing statements like Example 3.7, in addition to specifying a domain, we employ a device analogous to the universal quantifier, called the "existential quantifier." We will be using the symbol '∨' for the existential quantifier (another symbol commonly used for this purpose is '∃', a backward '*E*' for "existential"). Example 3.7 may thus be transcribed as follows:

> *Example 3.7a.* ∨*x* (*x* has lung disease)
> Domain: big-city dwellers

The existential quantifier in 3.7a may be read as "for at least one *x* . . ."; "there is at least one *x*, such that . . ."; or "some *x* are . . . ." The last of these readings is a bit misleading, since it diverges in two ways from the meaning of "there is at least one *x*, such that . . . ." First, the English expression "some *x* are . . ." is understood to imply that there are at least two *x*'s with the property in question. For example, we would hardly take the statement "Some logicians are well rounded" to be true if in the entire world there was only one logician who knew a thing or two about Mozart and the Beatles, in addition to logic. The truth of this English sentence seems to demand the existence of a minimum of two well-rounded logicians, where even two would be barely sufficient. Second, the English expression "some *x* are . . ." always also implies " . . . but not all *x* are . . . ." Anyone who says, "Some projects of the chemical division are environmentally friendly" also implies, albeit indirectly, that not *all* projects of the chemical division are particularly environmentally friendly. But the existential quantifier *does not* imply "and not all"; it only asserts the existence of at least one x with the relevant property, without saying anything about how many more than one there might happen to be.

The symbol for the existential quantifier bears a noncoincidental resemblance to the symbol for disjunction. There is a significant connection, for Example 3.7a simply asserts,

> *Example 3.7b:* Big-city dweller$_1$ has lung disease, ∨
> big-city dweller$_2$ has lung disease, ∨
> big-city dweller$_3$ has lung disease, ∨ . . .

As the expression "there is at least one *x*, such that . . ." is often used, it makes sense to attribute this meaning to the existential qualifier; indeed, this very expression has already put in an appearance in several earlier definitions. The variable following the existential quantifier is once again called a "bound individual variable" and is said to be bound by the existential quantifier.

Exercise 3.3. Rewrite the following statements by means of existential quantifiers and appropriate domains (some may have more than one correct transcription):

1. Some houses are pretty.
2. Some things are pretty.
3. Someone is climbing the Matterhorn.
4. Fred sees someone.
5. Someone sees Fred.
6. Karl-Adam sometimes lies.
7. No one is in the house.
8. No one knows the thief.
9. There is no rose without thorns.
10. There are some nice cities between North Cape and Sicily.
11. There are dogs and cats.

Exercise 3.4. Rewrite the following predicates in the least cumbersome colloquial language possible. Let the domain be "people."

1. $\wedge x$ (*x* trusts *y*)
2. $\wedge y$ (*x* trusts *y*)
3. $\wedge x$ (*x* distrusts *y*)
4. $\wedge y$ (*x* distrusts *y*)
5. $\vee x$ (*x* trusts *y*)
6. $\vee y$ (*x* trusts *y*)
7. $\wedge y$ (*x* punches *y*)

＊*Exercise 3.5.* Use the two-place predicates "*x* loves *y*," "*x* knows *y*," and "*x* helps *y*" to express the following one-place predicates:

1. *x* is a misanthrope.
2. *x* is a household name.
3. *x* is a philanthropist.
4. *x* runs with the in crowd.
5. *x* is not unliked.
6. *x* is an idol.
7. *x* isn't a complete unknown.
8. *x* is on a Mother Theresa trip.
9. Everyone helps *x* out.
10. *x* is there to help.

d. Supplementary Remarks on the Introduction of the Quantifiers

Several additional observations are required to complete the introduction of the quantifiers.

1. Statement logic got its name from the fact that the repeated occurrence of constituent statements determines the validity of statement-logical inferences. Analogously, predicate logic gets its name from the fact that the repeated occurrence of predicates is part of the "mechanism" of predicate-logical inferences. The quantifiers are an equally essential part of the same mechanism, and so predicate logic is often called "quantifier logic."

2. Clearly, the division of primitive statements into singular, universal, and existential statements does not completely exhaust the possible quantitative distinctions among them. The following statement, for example, does not fit neatly or effortlessly into any of the boxes described so far:

Example 3.8.   There are exactly nine planets in the solar system.

One way of accommodating such examples in an exhaustive classification of primitive statements would be to introduce special quantifiers. We might institute one quantifier for "There is exactly one *x*, such that . . . ," another for "There are exactly two *x*, such that . . . ," and so on. But it is unlikely any such scheme would satisfy us in the long term, since we would still have to deal with such statements as "There are more than ten x with property A" or "There are between seven and twenty-nine x with property B." The resulting logic would have to contain an infinite number of different quantifiers. Fortunately, a much more elegant way of expressing such quantitative relationships within predicate logic has been discovered. All that is required is *one* additional element, the identity '(=)'. This enables us to assert of objects a and b that they are either identical, $a = b$, or different, $\neg(a = b)$. Together with the two quantifiers, the identity allows us to capture all of the quantitative information in the above examples. The resulting logic is called "predicate logic with identity."

> ✳ *Exercise 3.6.* Express the following statements using quantifiers and the identity.
>
>   1. There are more than two democracies.
>   2. There are exactly two sexes.
>   This task requires connectives, as explained in the next remark.
>   3. Statement and predicate logic may be combined by simply employing connectives and quantifiers simultaneously. This is easily illustrated with the following example:

> *Example 3.9.*   At least one philosopher lives in Pittsburgh.

This statement may be understood as asserting the existence of at least one person who both lives in Pittsburgh and is a philosopher. With the help of existential quantifier and conjunction, this reading may be rendered:

> *Example 3.9a.* $\lor x$ (x lives in Pittsburgh $\land$ x is a philosopher)
>   Domain: people

The expression "x lives in Pittsburgh $\land$ x is a philosopher" may thus be construed as a *single* predicate, one which applies to an individual a just in case both the predicate "x lives in Pittsburgh" and the predicate "x is a philosopher" also apply to a. This may seem like a needlessly complex way of analyzing a fairly straightforward statement, but we recall that conjunction was originally introduced as a *sentential* connective. Now we are using it to compose *predicates* as well. All of the other connectives may also be used to compose predicates in similar fashion. The somewhat artificial rendition of 3.9 as 3.9a is not the only context in which the use of connectives to form compound predicates is called for, as the following remark should make clear.

4. The use of connectives allows us to expand or contract the domain over which an individual variable ranges, without changing the meaning of the statement and therefore without changing its truth value. We will have need of this method later (see Remark 9). Consider the following example:

Example 3.10.   There is at least one peace-loving person.

Calling on the existential quantifier, the most obvious transcription of this statement is,

Example 3.10a. $\lor x$ (x is peace-loving)
                Domain: people

But the same statement may be written as follows for the much broader domain of life forms:

Example 3.10b. $\lor x$ (x is a person $\land$ x is peace-loving)
                Domain: life forms

Example 3.10b asserts exactly the same thing as 3.10a. A necessary condition for this sameness of meaning (though not a sufficient condition) is that 3.10b is true under exactly the same circumstances as 3.10a. For 3.10b to be true, we must find a member of the domain of life forms that is both a person and peace-loving. An exceptionally peace-loving white dove will not do the trick, as it fails to satisfy the first conjunct. This example reveals the rule for expanding the domains of existential statements:

Rule for expanding the domain of an existential statement:

Reformulate the original domain of the existential quantifier as a predicate, and form the conjunction of this predicate with the original predicate.

Expanding the domains of universal statements requires a different rule. Consider the following example:

Example 3.11. All philosophers can perform a handstand.

The most straightforward transcription is:

Example 3.11a. $\bigwedge x$ (*x* can perform a handstand)
Domain: philosophers

For purposes of expanding the domain to the set of persons, the fact that 3.11 is most likely false need not concern us. Let us attempt this expansion as before, by means of conjunction:

Example 3.11b. $\bigvee x$ (*x* is a philosopher $\wedge$ *x* can perform a handstand)
Domain: people

But when is *this* statement true? Clearly, it is true when every single member of the domain of people is both a philosopher and a master of the handstand. This is obviously not what we wanted to say in 3.11a. There the claim was only that those people who turn out to be philosophers are handstand-capable. Let us attempt to express this state of affairs by means of the conditional:

Example 3.11c. $\bigwedge x$ (*x* is a philosopher $\rightarrow$ *x* can perform a handstand)
Domain: people

As *x* ranges over the domain of people, it also ranges over those who are not philosophers. For such individuals, the conditional expression in parentheses is true, regardless of whether they can perform a handstand or not, because its antecedent is false. On the other hand, for the philosophers in the domain, the expression in parentheses is only true if the consequent of the conditional is true—that is, if the philosopher in question can actually perform a handstand. And this is precisely what we wanted to claim on behalf of all philosophers in 3.11. The rule for expanding the domains of universal statements is thus as follows:

Rule for expanding the domain of a universal statement:

Reformulate the original domain of the universal quantifier as a predicate and place it in the antecedent of a conditional expression, whose consequent is the original predicate.

5. This rule for domain expansion can help us to solve an apparent problem with our definition of the universal quantifier. Let us suppose that there are no *real* philosophers, only people who are paid to act the part. In that case, the truth value of Example 3.11, "All philosophers can perform a handstand," appears *undetermined,* since when there are no philosophers, there is no way of answering the question "Can all philosophers perform a handstand?" But what happens if we mechanically carry out a domain expansion on 3.11a, converting it into 3.11c without first asking whether there are any philosophers? Example 3.11c, "$\wedge x(x$ is a philosopher $\rightarrow x$ can perform a handstand); Domain: people" *does* have a truth value. It is true, since by assumption the antecedent of the conditional is false for all elements of the domain. So if 3.11a and 3.11c are supposed to have exactly the same meaning, we must accept the convention that if there are no philosophers, 3.11a is *true.* Put in general terms, the convention is as follows:

Convention:

The statement "$\wedge xFx$; Domain D" is true when $D = \varnothing$ (the empty set).

This convention allows for the unrestricted application of our rules for expanding and contracting domains, without having to worry about the possibility of empty domains.

6. The convention introduced above constitutes a significant departure from that portion of so-called classical logic, which most closely corresponds to predicate logic. Syllogistic logic, which dates back to Aristotle, always operates under the assumption that when we utter a sentence like "All *S* are *P*," the set of *S*s is not empty; there is at least one *S*. This assumption is a natural consequence of the fact that syllogistic logic is geared toward everyday speech, in which claiming that "All *S* are *P*" tacitly and transparently commits us to the existence of at least one *S*. Someone who asserts, for example, "All Higgs particles mass at least 50 protons" is tacitly assuming the existence of Higgs particles. If, however, there are no Higgs particles, it is not clear what we should make of this statement. It appears neither true nor false. If we wanted to leave the existence of Higgs particles an open question, we would have to flesh out the above sentence by adding some such phrase as "provided they exist in the first place" or run the risk of misleading our listeners. (And, yes, dear reader, I am well aware that this example serves as a painful reminder that you yourself may not yet have made up your mind about the existence of Higgs particles.) Predicate logic, by contrast, is oriented more toward mathematical language, in which we may make a statement of the form "All *S* are *P*" without any implicit assumptions regarding the existence of *S*s. In mathematics, the statement "All *S* are *P*" is considered (trivially) true when there are no *S*s (the reasons for treating universal statements this way within mathematics need not concern us further here).

From this difference between syllogistic logic and predicate logic it follows that some inferences recognized as valid in one logic will not be considered valid by the other. In syllogistic logic, for example, the following inference is valid:

Example 3.12. All *A* are *B*
All *B* are *C*
*
Therefore,   Some *C* are *A*

In this example, "Some C are A" represents the standard way of express-ing "There is at least one C that is A" within syllogistic logic. And infer-ence 3.12 is *valid* within this same system, since syllogistic logic requires us to treat the truth of the premise "All A are B" as implying the existence of at least one A. The first premise also asserts that all such As are Bs. Since by the second premise they are also Cs, it follows that there must be at least one C that is A, as asserted in the conclusion. The truth of the premises, as understood within syllogistic logic, thus guarantees the truth of the conclusion. In predicate logic, by contrast, inference 3.12 is *in-valid*, as the first premise fails to guarantee the existence of any As. If there are no As, the first premise is trivially true, but the conclusion is false—the inference fails the test of validity.

But in the end, this difference between syllogistic logic and modern predicate logic is not particularly exciting, and it is certainly not the sort of fact that might move us toward more profound reflections on the possi-ble relativity of logic. On the contrary, all we have shown is that statements in which certain existential presuppositions are implicit may have differ-ent consequences from statements in which such presuppositions are ab-sent.

7. Just as quantifiers and connectives may be used together, so we may also combine multiple quantifiers. Consider the following:

Example 3.13. All humans are mortal.

An obvious way to rewrite this statement might be:

Example 3.13a. $\bigwedge x$ (x is mortal)   Domain: humans

We could also make matters a little more complicated by demanding that we use the two-place predicate, "y is the death date of x." "x is mortal" would then become "x has some death date y" or, more precisely, "$\bigvee y$ (y is the death date of x)." Inserting this rendering into 3.13a yields the fol-lowing:

Example 3.13b. $\wedge x(\vee y$ (y is the death date of x))

        Domain$_x$: humans; Domain$_y$: dates

Here we find one quantifier nested behind another. Obviously, their domains are different and must be specified accordingly.

8. When multiple nested quantifiers occur, the order in which they occur is frequently significant. Consider what happens to Example 3.13b, intended as a gloss of "All humans are mortal," when the order of the quantifiers is changed:

Example 3.14. $\vee y(\wedge x$ (y is the death date of x))

        Domain$_x$: humans; Domain$_y$: dates

But what does 3.14 assert? Only that there is some date that counts as the death date for all humans. But from the human perspective, roughly speaking, this would amount to Armageddon (I say "roughly speaking" because 3.14 actually claims that there is a date on which *all* humans die, which is impossible, since many are already dead and, in some cases, such as that of Aristotle, for quite a long time!). The difference between 3.14 and 3.13b is thus hardly trivial.

❋*Exercise 3.7.* Rewrite the following statements using the predicate "y likes x":

    1. *a* and *b* like each other.

    2. *b* likes *a*, but not vice versa.

    3. *a* doesn't like himself.

    4. Someone likes *a*.

    5. Someone doesn't like *a*.

    6. *a* doesn't like anyone.

    7. Everyone likes *a*.

    8. Someone likes someone.

    9. Everyone likes someone.

    10. Someone is liked by everyone.

    11. No one likes everyone.

12. Someone is liked by no one.

13. Everyone likes himself.

9. A statement with multiple quantifiers may contain individual variables belonging to different domains. This is the case in both 3.13b and 3.14, in which x ranges over the domain of humans, and y over the domain of dates. Individual constants may likewise be drawn from domains other than those of the quantifiers. When such statements are abstracted to particular PFs, the PL formulas that represent them are said to belong to many-sorted predicate logic, because they make reference to different sorts of individuals. In single-sorted predicate logic, by contrast, there is only one sort of individual, and many metalogical definitions become significantly simpler. It would thus be desirable, if possible, to make do with single-sorted predicate logic. Fortunately, the technique for domain expansion covered in Point 4 above can be used to convert a statement with different sorts of individuals into a formula containing only one sort. The procedure, which requires three steps, can easily be applied to Example 3.14:

Step 1: We begin by defining our new domain as the union of all prior domains. The *union* of two sets, which we customarily represent using the symbol '$\cup$', is the set of all elements belonging to *either* of the two. For Example 3.14, the new domain will thus be the set {humans}$\cup${dates}, which we will henceforth call "*D.*"

Step 2: Next we change the domain of the variables bound by the first quantifier in 3.14 (also called the *outermost* quantifier), expanding it to encompass the entire new domain D. Since the outermost quantifier, which binds variable y, is existential, the rule introduced in Point 4 requires that we transform the old domain into a predicate, then form the conjunction of this predicate with the original predicate, yielding,

Example 3.14a. $\vee y(y$ is a date$\wedge \wedge x(y$ is the death date of $x))$

Domain$_x$: humans; Domain$_y$: D

Step 3: Now we proceed to expand the domain of the next outermost quantifier to encompass all of *D*. In the case of Example 3.14, this is the universal quantifier, which binds *x*. Our rule for expanding the domains of universal quantifiers requires that we transform the original domain into a predicate and place it in the antecedent of a conditional, whose consequent is the original predicate. This yields the following:

> **Example 3.14b.** $\lor y(y$ is a date $\land \land x(x$ is human $\rightarrow y$ is the death date
> for *x*))
> Domain$_x$: *D*; Domain$_y$: *D*

We have thus successfully moved Example 3.14 into the realm of single-sorted predicate logic. For examples containing still more quantifiers, we would have to expand each quantifier in succession, until all of them range over the same domain. Now, in one sense, converting 3.14 into 3.14b via domain expansion leaves the result more complicated than the original, as 3.14b contains more connectives. The chief advantage of a single-sorted predicate logic, its greater conceptual simplicity, only becomes evident when we proceed to metalogic (at any rate, it *would* become evident, *if* we went to the trouble of actually writing down the relevant definitions for many-sorted predicate logic, which turn out to be considerably more complicated than their single-sorted counterparts). Since our method of domain expansion permits us to reduce many-sorted predicate logic to single-sorted predicate logic without loss of generality, we will be content to develop the single-sorted variety.

If we wish to keep our predicate logic strictly single-sorted, we also will need to develop a further method for domain expansion, one equipped to deal with statements that refer to individuals from outside the domains of their bound variables. In a single-sorted predicate logic, *all* individuals must, in the end, belong to one and the same comprehensive domain. Consider:

> **Example 3.15.** Anthony eats a cookie.

What is meant here is clearly that there is some cookie, such that Anthony eats it. Reformulating this statement using the two-place predicate "*x* eats *y*" and the individual constant '*a*' (for 'Anthony') yields the following:

> *Example 3.15a.* $\vee$c(a eats c)
>
> Domain$_c$: cookies

Obviously, this particular *a* does not belong to the domain of cookies (no matter how sweet Anthony may be), so the domain must be expanded. One likely candidate is the union of the set of cookies with the set of humans, D = {cookies}$\cup${humans}. Our rule for domain expansion for existential statements yields this:

> *Example 3.15b.* $\vee$c(c is a cookie$\wedge$a eats c)
>
> Domain: D

Later on, when we extract a predicate form of this statement by abstracting away the meaning of '*a*', the fact that that individual a belongs to a particular subset of *D*, the set of humans, is lost; all that remains is the certainty that a belongs to the same domain as variable *c*. If we wish to preserve this information, we must add a conjunct specifying *a*'s humanity:

> *Example 3.15c.* a is a human $\wedge$ $\vee$c (c is a cookie $\wedge$ a eats c)
>
> Domain: D

With this step complete, Example 3.15 is ready for the abstraction process by which we extract the predicate forms of single-sorted predicate logic.

> *✳Exercise 3.8.* Reformulate the following sentences in a manner appropriate to single-sorted predicate logic using the predicate "*x* loves *y*."
>
> 1. Fred loves animals.
> 2. Some mountains are loved by all.
> 3. It is not true that everyone loves at least one animal.
> 4. Every car-lover loves not only him- or herself but also his or her car.

10. Up to now all of our examples have involved quantifiers binding individual variables, while the predicates ascribed to or denied of these individuals have always remained fixed. As such, these examples belong to what is called "elementary predicate logic" or "first-order predicate logic." But in some statements, in addition to variables ranging over the individuals in a given domain, there are also variables ranging over the predicates ascribed to (or denied of) these individuals. Consider the following example:

Example 3.16. Every thing has at least one property.

Or, in other words, for every thing, there is at least one property, such that the thing in question has the property. In addition to an individual variable, bound by a universal quantifier, ranging over the domain of all things, an analysis of this sentence calls for another variable, bound by an *existential* quantifier, ranging over the domain of all *properties,* which may be ascribed to or denied of these things. With such a predicate variable in place, we obtain the following:

Example 3.16a. $\wedge x (\vee F(x$ has property $F))$
Domain$_x$: things; Domain$_F$: properties

Example 3.16a belongs to what is called "second-order predicate logic," characterized by its use of bound variables ranging not only over individuals but also over the predicates used in talking about these individuals. "Third-order predicate logic" introduces a further level of variables and associated quantifiers, which range over the predicates used in talking about the predicates ascribed to (or denied of) the individuals in a particular domain. More generally, predicate logic from the second order on up is called "higher-order predicate logic," or "nth-order predicate logic," where n is the number of the highest order of bound variables. So in elementary or first-order predicate logic, variables may range only over individuals, while predicates are fixed; higher-order predicate logic drops this restriction. Higher-order predicate logic is, in many respects, far more complicated than elementary predicate logic, and we will not be concerned with it here.

1.2. Predicate Form
a. Definition

In what follows, we will introduce the notion of predicate form by strict analogy to the notion of statement form (compare section II.1.2). But in the context of predicate logic, more elaborate preparations are called for before we can move from a given statement to one of its predicate forms (PFs). To begin with, the statement must be analyzed using the tools developed in the previous section. In other words, it must be transcribed using quantifiers, bound individual variables, a single-sorted domain, individual constants, connectives, and predicates. This preparatory work is by far the most difficult step in the transition to a PF.

> *Exercise 3.9.* Rewrite the following statements using quantifiers, predicates, etc., analyzing each as thoroughly as possible. For example, instead of the predicate "x loves all people," use "$\wedge y$ (x loves y); Domain$_y$: people."
>
> 1. If wishes were horses, then beggars would ride.
> 2. A penny saved is a penny earned.
> 3. Early to bed and early to rise makes a man healthy, wealthy, and wise.
> 4. An apple a day keeps the doctor away.
> 5. He who lives by the sword, dies by the sword.
> 6. Curiosity killed the cat.

With such preparations complete, the transition to a PF is relatively simple. Before demonstrating the process, I offer the following definition for a PF of a statement:

> **Definition 3.8.** A predicate form (PF) of a statement is obtained by abstracting away the contents of the domain (the number and kind of individuals in it), the meanings of the predicates, and the meanings of the individual

constants, leaving only the place number of the predicates and the identity and difference of predicates and individual constants as part of the PF.

Once again, the close parallel to statement logic (Definition 2.1) is clear: in both cases, meaning itself is abstracted away, but sameness or difference in meaning is preserved. The role played by the repeated occurrence of constituent statements in statement logic is now being played by the repeated occurrence of individual variables, individual constants, and predicates. Their identity and difference must thus be preserved. The instructions for abstracting PFs also imply that quantifiers belong to predicate form. In other words, the transition to a logical form does not abstract away the quantity of a statement. Finally, because we have decided to confine ourselves to single-sorted predicate logic (compare section II.1.1.d, Point 9), definition 3.8 refers unambiguously to "*the* domain."

Like SFs before them, PFs are represented by means of formulas. These require two sorts of letters:

* Letters *a, b, c* . . . will be called *individual placeholders, schematic individual letters,* or *free individual variables.* They are used wherever individual constants occurred prior to abstraction. The expression "free individual variable" is perhaps a bit misleading, since these letters really are *placeholders* and, unlike bound individual variables, do not range over an entire domain. Later on, however, individual constants will also grow legs, allowing them to run through their respective domains, and so we may as well get used to calling them "free individual variables." This will allow us to use the shorthand expression "individual variable" to encompass both individual placeholders and bound individual variables.

* Letters '*A*', '*B*', '*C*' . . . will be called "predicate placeholders" or "schematic predicate letters." They are used wherever predicates occurred prior to abstraction. So, when letter '*A*' occurs within a PF, it serves not as an abbreviation for a predicate but as a placeholder. The individual letters (or, more generally, individual variables) to which the predicate letter refers are always placed after the predicate letter itself. For example, the one-place

> predicate letter *'F'* might occur within *'Fa'*, or the two-place predicate letter *'R'* within *'Rxy'*.

Let us now consider a few simple examples of the transition from a statement to a corresponding PF, using a wavy arrow ('$\rightsquigarrow$') to represent the abstraction process (note that this is *not* a standard notational device). For example 3.4, "Socrates is a man," no further preparation is necessary. Using the schematic individual letter *'a'* as a placeholder for the individual constant 'Socrates' and the schematic predicate letter *'M'* (or *'Mx'*, if we include the individual variable *'x'*) as a placeholder for "*x* is a man," we obtain the following:

> ***Example 3.17.*** Socrates is a man $\rightsquigarrow$ *Ma*

Since Definition 3.8 demands that the place number of the predicate "*x* is a man" not be abstracted away, we note that it has been preserved by virtue of the fact that only *one* individual letter, *'a'*, follows the predicate letter *'M'*. In general, an n-place predicate letter will be followed by *n* individual letters or individual variables;

> ***Example 3.18.*** *y* is the death date of *x* $\rightsquigarrow$ *Tyx*

The order of individuals as they appear in the logical subject must be respected, so it is preserved by the order in which the corresponding individual letters or variables follow the predicate letter. As a final example, let us consider the transition to a PF for Example 3.14b, our prediction of Armageddon. A mnemonically helpful choice of predicate letters is in order, so we will use *'Ax'* for "*x* is a date," *'Hx'* for "*x* is human," and *'Dxy'* for "*x* is the death date of *y*."

> ***Example 3.19.*** $\vee y(y$ is a date $\wedge \wedge x(x$ is a human $\rightarrow y$ is the death date
> of x)); Domain$_{x,y}$: D
> $\rightsquigarrow \vee y(Ay \wedge \wedge x (Hx \rightarrow Dyx))$

The domain, along with the original meanings of the predicates, have disappeared from the resulting formula. What remains are the quantifiers, the connectives, the parentheses, and identity and difference of individual variables and predicate letters, and the place numbers of the predicates.

b. Further Remarks on the Notion of Predicate Form

1. Just like SFs, the PFs of a statement lack truth value. Once again, the reason is that over the course of the transition to a PF, we have abstracted away components of the statement indispensable to its being either true or false.

2. In representing a PF, we must always use the same predicate and individual letters for the same predicates and individuals, and different predicate and individual letters for different predicates and individuals. This requirement has its exact parallel in statement logic. As in statement logic, *determining* the relevant identities and differences sometimes poses problems.

3. In general, there is no single, unequivocal PF for a given statement. Let us return to Example 3.15:

Example 3.15. Anthony eats a cookie.

In section II.1.1d, this example paved the way for the introduction of formalization in single-sorted predicate logic. Using the two-place predicate "x eats y," we arrived at the following:

Example 3.15c. a is a human $\land \lor c$ (c is a cookie $\land$ a eats c)   Domain: D

We may further abstract this statement to obtain a PF:

Example 3.15d. $Ha \land \lor c$ ($Cc \land Eac$)

However, if instead we use the one-place predicate "x eats a cookie," we obtain the following:

Example 3.15e. a eats a cookie

Which may then be abstracted to yield the PF:

> *Example 3.15f.* Ca

And so we cannot, strictly speaking, talk of *the* PF of a statement, any more than we could talk of *the* SF of a statement, because there are often many possibilities.

4. We turn to the definitions of four useful concepts, commonly used in predicate logic. First, continuing to follow the model of statement logic, we define the notion of a PL formula:

> *Definition 3.9.* A representation of a PF by means of individual variables, individual letters, predicate letters, quantifiers, connectives, and parentheses, is called a "predicate-logical (or PL) formula."

An example of a somewhat more complex formula is this:

> *Example 3.20.* $\lor x(\land y\,(Ky{\rightarrow}Gxy)\land\land z(\neg Sz{\rightarrow}\neg Gxz))$

A given quantifier pertains only to the subformula immediately following it. In Example 3.20, the universal quantifier with respect to y pertains to the subformula $(Ky{\rightarrow}Gxy)$, the universal quantifier with respect to z to the subformula $(\neg Sz{\rightarrow}\neg Gxz)$, while the existential quantifier pertains to the entire expression enclosed by the outermost pair of parentheses. We are led to the following definition:

> *Definition 3.10.* The subformula immediately following a quantifier, to which that quantifier pertains, is called the "scope" of the quantifier.

Finally, we may distinguish between PFs that contain schematic individual letters, and those that do not:

> *Definition 3.11.* PL formulas containing (unbound) schematic individual letters are called "open formulas"; all others are called "closed formulas."

Example 3.20 and the formula '$\land xFx$' are examples of closed formulas. 'Fa' and '$\lor xTxb$' are examples of open formulas.

5. There are both similarities and differences between the notions of grammatical and predicate-logical form. Consider this statement:

Example 3.21.   Marvin runs.

In the case of this singular statement, grammatical form and PF are indistinguishable; the grammatical subject is the logical subject, and the grammatical predicate is the logical predicate. The grammatical form might be represented as "Subject-Predicate," and the PF as *'Rm'*. But now consider the following:

Example 3.22.   Nobody runs.

Plainly, the grammatical form of 3.22 is identical to that of 3.21. But the PFs are very different. The reason for this is that 'nobody' is not an individual name and so, unlike 3.21, 3.22 *is not* a singular statement but a negated existential statement. Rewriting it with this in mind, we obtain the following:

Example 3.22a.   It is not the case that ($\vee x$ (x runs); Domain: humans)

Which straightforwardly yields the PF:

Example 3.22b. $\neg \vee x Rx$

Analogously, one straightforward PF for "Somebody runs" is "$\vee x Rx$," reading the "somebody" as asserting the existence of at least one person who runs. For a further example of the difference between grammatical form and PF, we return to

Example 3.15.   Anthony eats a cookie.

While the grammatical form of this statement is "Subject-Predicate-Object," the most straightforward PFs are *'Ca'* and *'Ha*$\wedge\vee c(Cc\wedge Eac)$*'*.

c. An Example of a Relatively Complex PL Formalization

The following demonstration of a fairly complex PL formalization serves to illustrate how logical reflection, or the contemplation of the logical forms of a statement, can help elucidate the meaning of the statement. Statement logic provided us with a similar experience (compare section II.1.2.b, Point 5). The statement to be formalized is this:

> *Example 3.23.*   In egalitarian societies, some of the laws of class societies fail to hold.

The meaning of this statement seems clear enough—now let us see whether logical analysis confirms this first impression. In preparation for the transition to a PF, we begin with a series of questions.

1. Does 3.23 contain any independent constituent statements joined by connectives? Apparently not. Therefore, our analysis will rely exclusively on the tools of predicate logic.

2. Is this (truth-functionally primitive) statement singular, universal, or existential? Answering this question is the first step toward the transition to a PF. The most straightforward response (though by no means the only possibility) is to treat 3.23 as an existential statement:

> *Example 3.23a.*   There are some laws of class societies that fail to hold in egalitarian societies.

3. Now, what exactly is being said about this law, or these laws, whose existence has been asserted? More technically, what is being predicated of them? Two things: they are laws of class societies (hereafter CS), and they fail to hold in egalitarian societies (hereafter ES).

4. How are the two predications combined? It is plausible to suppose that our statement asserts their *conjunction*: the law or laws in question are both laws of CS *and* laws that fail to hold in ES. But what is a "law of CS"? Plainly, it is a law that *does* hold for CS. By this reasoning, we rewrite 3.23a as follows:

Example 3.23b. $\vee x(x$ holds for CS and x does not hold for ES)

    Domain: laws

3.23b suggests a plausible PF for 3.23:

Example 3.23c. $\vee x(Cx \wedge \neg Sx)$

But in view of the fact that both predicates in 3.23b involve holding for one sort of society or another, still further analysis is possible.

5. In how many CSs and ESs is the law in question meant to hold, and fail to hold, respectively? Now it gets tricky. Does the phrase "laws of class societies" in 3.23 apply to laws that hold in *all* CSs? Or are these laws merely *characteristic* of class societies in the sense that they fail to apply to other forms of society, even though they do not universally apply to *all* members of the class CS? Predicate-logical reflection thus reveals a certain lack of clarity in 3.23. It is not at all evident what, exactly, "laws of class societies" is supposed to mean. Further, our interpretation of this phrase significantly affects our understanding of 3.23. For if we take it to refer to laws that are *characteristic* of CS in the aforementioned sense, and thus apply *exclusively* to members of CS, then 3.23 is trivial: of course such laws will fail to hold in ES. So, let us take "laws of class societies" to be laws that hold in *all* class societies, leaving open whether they apply in other forms of society as well. On this reading, we may rewrite the predicate "x holds for CS" in 3.23b as follows:

  $\wedge y$ (x holds for $\acute{y}$) Domain$_y$: CS

Because we will soon be speaking of societies outside of CS, it behooves us to expand our domain to encompass all societies. In accordance with our rule for domain expansion (see section II.1.1d, Point 4), we obtain:

  $\wedge y(y$ is a CS $\rightarrow x$ holds for $y)$ Domain$_y$: Societies

With regard to the specific law, or laws, in question, 3.23 is fairly clear as to their applicability to ES: They are meant *not* to apply to *any* of the societies in this class (the best that can be said on this score is that 3.23 is *fairly* clear; it might be thought to assert that the law or laws in question fail to hold for *all* ESs). The 3.23b predicate "*x* does not hold for ES" may thus be rewritten:

$\bigwedge z$ (*x* does not hold for *z*)   Domain$_z$: ES

Expanding the domain to encompass all societies yields,

$\bigwedge z$ (*z* is an ES → *x* does not hold for *z*)   Domain$_z$: Societies

Finally, we unpack the negation in the consequent of the conditional:

$\bigwedge z$ (*z* is an ES → ¬(*x* holds for *z*))   Domain$_z$: Societies

Now we may insert our two partial results into 3.23b:

Example 3.23d: $\bigvee x (\bigwedge y(y$ is a CS → (*x* holds for *y*)$\wedge \bigwedge z(z$ is an ES →¬(*x* holds for *z*)))

Domain$_x$: Laws; Domain$_{y,z}$: Societies

6. Our current formalization still retains the cumbersome reference to two separate domains. A further domain expansion is called for. Applying our rules for domain expansion with a view toward the domain $D = $ {Laws}$\cup${Societies}, and using "Soc" for "society," we obtain the following:

Example 3.23e. $\bigvee x(x$ is a Law $\wedge (\bigwedge y(y$ is a Soc → (*y* is a CS → *x* holds for *y*)) $\wedge \bigwedge z(z$ is an S → (*z* is an ES →¬(*x* holds for *z*)))))

Domain$_{x,y,z}$: D

7. The final transition to a PF is child's play, the selection of appropriate predicate letters being the only remaining intellectual challenge. We are fortunate in that the relevant English expressions all have different initial letters, allowing us to use '*L*' for "law," '*S*' for "society," '*C*' for "class society," '*H*' for "hold," and '*E*' for "egalitarian society."

Example 3.23f. $\vee x(Lx \wedge (\wedge y(Sy \to (Cy{\to}Hxy)) \wedge \wedge z(Sz{\to}(Ez{\to}\neg Hxz))))$

We conclude this section by focusing briefly on the way in which reflecting on the logical form of a statement helps to illuminate the statement's meaning. The clarification is significant. For example, as we discovered in our analysis of 3.23, careful consideration of quantifier placement can reveal hidden fuzziness or ambiguity. But however highly we might esteem such contributions of formal logic, we must also recognize that, in one important respect, they are fundamentally limited. For it is not only the *relationships* among the concepts in a given statement that demand clarification but also the concepts themselves. In the case of 3.23, for example, we ought to ask what class societies and egalitarian societies really *are,* not to mention what sort of social laws we are talking about. When it comes to these questions, formal logic is of little help, for its contribution can only really begin when we have abstracted away the meanings of the concepts.

1.3. The Interpretation of PFs

In broad outline, our procedure in the following section will mirror that of section II.1.3, in our treatment of statement logic. As before, we will distinguish intensional from extensional interpretation (where, once again, it is the extensional interpretations that turn out to be of interest to our exposition of valid inference). However, the considerable differences between SFs and PFs will lead to marked deviations in matters of technical detail.

a. Intensional Interpretation

The intensional interpretation of a PL formula involves the complete reversal of the abstraction process by which the formula was obtained from a statement. This requires that we specify a domain (one will do, provided our predicate logic is single sorted), an individual for each of the individual letters, and a predicate for each of the predicate letters. For the sake of tidiness, let us state these requirements in the form of a definition:

Definition 3.12. An intensional interpretation of a PL formula consists in the specification of a domain, in the assignment of individual names to individual letters, and predicate intensions to predicate letters, for all individual and predicate letters in the formula; the same individual names and predicate intensions must always be assigned to the same individual and predicate letters.

If the result of intensional interpretation is to be a statement in the strict logical sense—a sentence with definite truth value—the various assignments must also fit each other. In other words, the chosen individuals must actually belong to the chosen domain, and the chosen predicates must actually apply to, or fail to apply to, every element of the domain (or, for n-place predicates, to every n-tupel of domain elements). Only in this way can we be sure that the interpreted formula will actually have a truth value. To illustrate, suppose we intensionally interpreted the formula '$\lor xFx$' as follows: Domain: natural numbers; *Fx: x* is liquid. As interpreted, the formula would assert that there is at least one liquid natural number. But in the strict logical sense, this sentence is not a statement at all, as the liquidity predicate neither applies nor fails to apply to natural numbers. The sentence is neither true nor false; it is nonsense.

This concludes our brief discussion of the intensional interpretation of PFs. Our treatment of extensional interpretation will not be quite so swift.

b. Extensional Interpretation

Just as in statement logic, the idea of an extensional interpretation in predicate logic is to reverse just enough of the abstraction process leading to a PL formula, such that a truth value is assigned to the formula as a whole. In statement logic, all this took was an assignment of a truth value to each sentential letter. Predicate logic demands a great deal more effort. There are four steps.

1. We begin with one of the victims of the abstraction process, the *do-*

main. From this set are drawn the elements to which the predicates are ascribed, or of which they are denied. For purposes of extensional interpretation, the minimal assignment of a domain D consists in a specification of the number of elements in D. In accordance with the standard notational practice of set theory, finite sets are represented by listing their elements in series, with ellipses, and placing the list in wavy brackets. So if set D contains m elements, $a_1 \ldots a_m$, it is written as $D = \{a_1 \ldots a_m\}$, where m is the natural number corresponding to the number of elements in D. When D contains (countably) infinitely many elements, we write it as $D = \{a_1, a_2, a_3 \ldots\}$, where the ellipsis indicates a series without end (needless to say, in any concrete specification of an infinite series, it must be clear which elements follow a_3). The first stage in the extensional interpretation of a PL formula thus consists in assigning as domain a set unspecified except with regard to the number of elements in it, either $D = \{a_1 \ldots a_m\}$ or $D = \{a_1, a_2, a_3 \ldots\}$.

2. Next, for open formulas, every *individual letter* must be assigned to a specific element of D, as specified in Step 1.

3. The schematic *predicate letters* are next in line. We begin with the predicate letters introduced in place of abstractions from one-place predicates. In order to assign a truth value to an expression of the form Fa, for some a in D, we must know whether or not a is in the extension of F (if it is, Fa is true; otherwise it is false). For purposes of the extensional interpretation of PL formulas, we simply assign to each one-place predicate letter a *predicate extension:* the subset of D, to whose elements the predicate may correctly be ascribed. The extensional interpretation of a one-place predicate letter thus does not require the assignment of a full-fledged predicate, including both an extension and a *predicate meaning*. Assigning a subset of the domain D is enough.

4. The procedure for interpreting predicate letters introduced in place of n-place predicates is substantially the same, though technically more complicated. An n-place predicate is a relation between n elements of a particular set, in this case the domain D. Accordingly, an n-place predi-

cate may be said to apply to particular n-tuples $(a_1 \ldots a_n)$, where the a_is are elements of D. So the extension of an n-place predicate is a set of n-tuples. The set of *all* n-tuples of elements of a particular set D is called the "n-way product of D with itself." It is written $D \times D \times D \ldots \times D$ or, more concisely, D^n (read "D to the n"). Using familiar set notation, we may also write D^n as

$$D^n = \{(a_1, \ldots, a_n) \mid a_i \in D, i = 1, \ldots, n\}.$$

In other words, D^n is a set (indicated by the wavy brackets) containing elements of the form $(a_1, \ldots, a_n)$, each of which has the following property (described by the expression following the vertical stroke): for all i between 1 and n, a_i is an element of D. As should now be clear, the extension of an n-place predicate is a subset of D^n. Accordingly, the extensional interpretation of a PL formula assigns a subset of D^n to every predicate letter introduced in place of an abstracted n-place predicate.

The extensional interpretation of a PL formula, as outlined above, is captured in the following definition:

Definition 3.13. The extensional interpretation of a PL formula consists in the assignment of a (finite or infinite) set D as domain, of elements of D to the individual letters, and of predicate extensions to the predicate letters (where each n-place predicate letter is assigned a subset of D^n); the same elements and subsets must always be assigned to the same individual and predicate letters.

Plainly, the extensional interpretation of a PL formula is both necessary and sufficient for assigning that formula a truth value. For PL formulas consist in nothing but open subformulas of the form Fa, closed subformulas of the form Gx (to use a one-place example), connectives, and quantifiers. The assignment of extensions to the predicate letters determines truth values for both sorts of subformulas, taking quantifiers into account for the closed subformulas. And since the connectives are truth-functional, the truth value of entire formulas is also determined.

A further example serves to illustrate the process. Consider the following open formula:

Example 3.24: $\vee x((Ax \rightarrow Cx) \wedge Aa)$

Let this formula be extensionally interpreted as follows (It is hoped that my esteemed readers will not be distracted by the *complete arbitrariness* of this interpretation. There is simply no point in asking, "Why interpret the formula in precisely this way? Is there any reason?"):

1. Let the domain contain nine elements, $a_1, \ldots, a_9$, or $D = \{a_1, \ldots, a_9\}$. No further description of the a_i is called for.

2. Let element a_2 be assigned to individual letter a.

3. Let the set $E_A = \{a_1, \ldots, a_5\} \subset D$ be assigned as the extension of predicate letter A. Writing the extensionally interpreted predicate letter A as "A_I," we observe that $A_I a_1$ is true, as are $A_I a_2, \ldots, A_I a_5$. Let the set $E_C = \{a_5, \ldots, a_9\} \subset D$ be assigned as the extension of predicate letter C.

4. As the sample formula contains no n-place predicate letters for $n > 1$, the final step may be waived.

Under this interpretation, formula 3.24 should have a definite truth value; this, after all, is what extensional interpretation is for. But which truth value? Because 3.24 is an existential statement, we must search domain D with a view toward discovering an element x such that $(A_I x \rightarrow C_I x) \wedge A_I a_2$ is true (Recall that A_I and C_I stand for interpreted A and C, respectively, and a_2 is the element of D assigned to a). $(A_I x \rightarrow C_I x) \wedge A_I a_2$ is a conjunction, and since a_2 lies within E_A, $A_I a_2$ is true. So $(A_I x \rightarrow C_I x) \wedge A_I a_2$ is true just in case the first conjunct is true—just in case we find an x, which makes $A_I x \rightarrow C_I x$ true. Finally, $A_I x \rightarrow C_I x$ is true just in case either $A_I x$ is false or $C_I x$ true. $A_I x$ is false for $x = a_6, \ldots, a_9$, and $C_I x$ is true for $x = a_5, \ldots, a_9$. And so, on the given interpretation, formula 3.24 is true: the existential claim is satisfied by $x = a_5, \ldots, a_9$.

c. Truth Analysis

In general, evaluating the truth value of a given formula on a given extensional interpretation is considerably more involved for PL formulas than it was for SL formulas. Our discussion of the previous example gives us an inkling of the complexities involved. In statement logic, the truth analysis of an extensionally interpreted formula with n connectives takes at most n steps. Each step consists in the assignment of a truth value to one subformula, accomplished by writing the truth value beneath the appropriate connective, so that with n connectives we are done after n steps. By contrast, in the truth analysis of a PL formula, the number of steps depends crucially on the size of the domain assigned to the formula by the given interpretation. If the formula contains a universal quantifier, the variable bound by this quantifier must run through the entire domain. If the domain is infinite, then barring shortcuts, the truth analysis requires infinitely many steps.

But the difference between statement logic and predicate logic becomes even more dramatic when we contemplate the truth analysis of a given formula *under all* extensional interpretations. In our treatment of the metalogic of predicate logic, just as in the metalogic of statement logic, we will have to account for all possible extensional interpretations. In statement logic, for a formula with m different sentential letters, we must evaluate its truth value under 2^m possible interpretations (see section II.1.3.c). And as noted above, the truth analysis of a given formula takes no more than n steps per interpretation, where n is the number of connectives. So the complete truth analysis of an SL formula with m different sentential letters and n connectives takes at most $2^m \bullet n$ steps. For short formulas, this number is not too large. For example, in exercise 2.12, the most labor-intensive cases involved three sentential letters and five connectives, and so their truth analysis under all possible interpretations called for no more than $2^3 \bullet 5 = 40$ steps. The truth analysis of longer formulas may safely be left to a computer, given the "mechanical," hence easily programmable, nature of the procedure.

But in predicate logic, the situation with regard to the possible interpretations of a given formula is radically different. For in predicate logic, even the simplest of formulas has *uncountably infinitely many* different extensional interpretations. In order to explain what this means, I must first elucidate the concept of the "uncountable infinite." In the realm of physical things, we generally encounter only finite sets, such as the five eggs in the fridge, or the twenty-two guests at the party, or the 5,400 flying ants in the bathroom. In mathematics, by contrast, we quickly run into infinite sets, perhaps none more familiar than the natural numbers, 1, 2, 3, etc. The presence of the "etc." signifies that the numbers never stop. They go on without end; they are infinite. But the infinity of infinite sets is frequently of the sort that allows the elements of such sets to be enumerated, with each element assigned its own natural number. For example, the set of prime numbers is infinite, but enumerable in the following way: the first prime number is 2, the second prime number is 3, the third prime number is 5, the fourth prime number is 7, and so on. Infinite sets that allow for this sort of enumeration are called "countably infinite."

At first blush, the enumerability of the elements of an infinite set seems to be a trivial matter. But this is far from the case. For it has been shown that there are infinite sets containing so many elements that they *cannot even be enumerated.* This means that we can demonstrate that no possible enumeration procedure will catch all the elements in the set, no matter how long we keep counting. Infinite sets with so many elements that they cannot be enumerated are called "uncountably infinite." Here are a few examples. The set of natural numbers, 1, 2, 3, . . . , is clearly countably infinite. The same holds of the whole numbers, . . . -3, -2, -1, 0, 1, 2, 3, . . . They may be counted as follows: 0, 1, -1, 2, -2, 3, etc. The set of rational numbers, or fractions of whole numbers, also turns out to be countably infinite. But the real numbers, by contrast, are uncountably infinite. These include all numbers representable as points on the number line, including such irrational numbers as p and the square root of 2. Furthermore, even every bounded real interval is uncountably infinite. And so the set of real numbers between 0 and 1, the set of numbers between 0 and 1 representable as infinite decimal fractions, is uncountably infinite. On the number line, this set can be said to contain all of the points within the interval from 0 to 1.

Before returning to predicate logic, we review one final mathematical result. There is a simple procedure for constructing an uncountably infinite set out of a countably infinite set. For a countably infinite set C (C for "countably infinite"), define U as the set of all subsets of C: $U = \{S \mid S \subset C\}$ (read: U is defined as the set of all Ss that are subsets of C). This set U, also known as the "power set" of C, has been shown to be uncountably infinite. In other words, the power set of a countably infinite set is uncountably infinite. This set-theoretic result is needed in order to show that every PL formula has uncountably infinitely many extensional interpretations.

To see this, consider the simplest of all PL formulas, 'Fa'; 'F' is a predicate letter, a an individual letter. In order to capture all of the possible interpretations of this formula, we must include all ranges of domain size, from one element, to two, all the way up to the domain with countably infinitely many elements. Further, for each such domain, the predicate letter F must be assigned every possible extension: every possible subset of D. Confining our attention to the countably infinite domain, we see that the set of possible extensions of 'F' is the power set of D, which by the above result contains the *uncountably infinitely many* subsets of D. So for this one countably infinite domain there are uncountably infinitely many possible extensions for 'F', thus *uncountably infinitely many extensional interpretations* of the formula 'Fa'.

Here, then, is one difference between statement and predicate logic: while every SL formula has only finitely many extensional interpretations, even the simplest PL formula has uncountably infinitely many. While this difference might appear purely quantitative, it turns out to have a fundamental *qualitative* difference as a consequence. We will return to this consequence in section III.2.2.

1.4. Summary

Our exposition of predicate logic has proceeded by strict analogy with the earlier presentation of statement logic. In statement logic we began by distinguishing the connectives; here we set out from the distinction between singular, universal, and existential statements. These distinctions served to extract features of statements relevant to logically valid inference: first the connectives and now the quantifiers as well. Next came the transition to logical form, in which the features of statements relevant to a particular class of inference were brought to the fore and everything else discarded. In statement logic, this basically amounted to abstracting away the meanings of constituent statements while retaining the connectives that joined them. In predicate logic, the meanings of predicates and individual names were basically abstracted away, leaving both connectives and quantifiers. Finally, the transition to logical form was partially reversed by means of extensional interpretation. The object of this sort of interpretation was to give back to each formula just enough of what it had lost to abstraction so as to restore its truth value. The construction of this admittedly odd procedure is justified by its utility in explicating metalogical concepts. In statement logic, extensional interpretation, and even the examination of all possible extensional interpretations of a given SL formula, were effectively mechanical. In predicate logic, concocting a single extensional interpretation is equally unproblematic. But when we contemplate the space of *all* interpretations of a given PL formula, we confront the fact that even the simplest formula has uncountably infinitely many different extensional interpretations. In consequence, we expect it to be much more difficult to say anything about all of the possible interpretations of a given PL formula than it was to articulate the corresponding notions in statement logic. The precise extent of this difficulty will be one of the major themes in our treatment of the metalogic of predicate logic.

2. The Metalogic of Predicate Logic

2.1. Parallels to the Metalogic of Statement Logic

Our procedure for explicating key notions in the metalogic of predicate logic will be strictly analogous to the procedure followed in statement logic. No new insights are required. Accordingly, many of the definitions in this section will be almost word-for-word identical with the corresponding definitions for statement logic. For here, as before, we are approaching metalogical concepts by way of a particular conception of logical form. So while our new definitions make reference to the forms and formulas of *predicate logic,* not statement logic, they are otherwise the same as their predecessors. However, any reference to the extensional interpretation of a PL formula must take into account the procedure articulated in section II.1.3.c, above, leading to one significant consequence.

2.2. Logical Truth

a. Definition

Our path to the definition of predicate-logical truth proceeds, as is customary, by way of an example.

> *Example 3.25.*   Every natural number is either prime or not prime.

This unremarkable and uninsightful sentence is not, of course, a substantive statement about the natural numbers, for of course every number is either divisible only by 1 and itself or it is not; it either has the feature in question or it lacks it. The truth of Example 3.25 emerges out of the statement itself, and no recourse to other statements or facts beyond this statement is required in order to ascertain that truth. We are dealing with a logical truth, but not a statement-logical truth, for 3.25 contains no extensionally joined constituent statements. Without the quantifying expression, "every natural number," the expression "is prime" is not a statement, for it lacks a logical subject. To be sure, applying the quantifier separately to each of the expressions following it would yield two extensionally joined constituent statements:

Example 3.26. Either every natural number is prime or every natural number is not prime.

But example 3.26 asserts something very different from 3.25, namely that either all natural numbers are prime or that all of them are not. And this clearly *is not* a logical truth, because it is not any kind of truth; it is a patent falsehood, since *some* numbers are prime and *some* are not. A straightforward logical form for 3.25 is the following:

Example 3.25a. $\wedge z(Pz \vee \neg Pz)$

Imagining the universal quantifier in 3.25a as expressing a series of conjunctions yields

Example 3.25b. $(Pz_1 \vee \neg Pz_1) \wedge (Pz_2 \vee \neg Pz_2) \wedge (Pz_3 \vee \neg Pz_3) \wedge \ldots$

Thus illustrating why 3.25 and 3.25a are logical truths: they express a conjunction of logical truths, albeit a conjunction of indefinite length, and thus not a proper conjunction at all. By contrast, the following PL form for 3.26 reveals more clearly why this statement *is not* a logical truth:

Example 3.26a. $\wedge zPz \vee \wedge z \neg Pz$

So 3.25a is a candidate example of a predicate-logically-true formula. In other words, this formula, like its statement logic counterparts, is meant to be true under all extensional interpretations, where of course we mean the sort of extensional interpretations appropriate to predicate logic. And, indeed, it is obvious that every extensional interpretation will assign the truth-value "true" to 3.25, for no matter how large the domain or what extension (what subset of the domain) is assigned to predicate letter P, $(Pz \vee \neg Pz)$ will be true for all z in the domain, because one of the two disjuncts will always be true; z either lies within the extension assigned to P or it does not. The logical truth of a PL formula thus amounts to nothing more than truth under all interpretations, where these must be thought to encompass all possible domains.

One further addendum is called for. There are some PL formulas we may want to classify as logically true, despite the fact that they are not quite true under *all* interpretations. Consider,

Example 3.27. $\wedge x Fx \rightarrow \vee y Fy$

This PL formula looks like it ought to be logically true, for if all the elements in a given domain D possess property F, then it is also the case that there is at least one element of the domain with property F—no matter what the domain is, or what extension is assigned to F. And yet 3.27 is false under an interpretation in which the domain is the empty set. For in accordance with the convention introduced in section II.1.1d, point 5, the antecedent of the conditional is true for the empty domain, but the consequent false, since this domain contains *no* elements, hence no elements with property F. So this interpretation with its empty domain prevents us from saying that 3.27 is true under *all* interpretations. But then, assigning the empty set as domain is a somewhat strange way to go about the business of interpreting PL formulas, and it lies within our power to simply rule this interpretation out of bounds, so as to keep it from making our lives more difficult. We will do this by requiring of predicate-logically-true formulas only that they be true under all interpretations with *non-empty* domains, and 3.27 satisfies this criterion. We are now ready to formulate our definition of predicate-logical truth:

Definition 3.14.

1. A PF or PL formula is called "predicate-logically (PL-) true" or "valid" just in case it is true under all extensional interpretations with non-empty domains.

2. A statement is called "predicate-logically true" or "valid" just in case (at least) one of its PFs is a PL-truth.

The symbol for SL-truth is the same as that used for PL-truth, '⊨'. To avoid confusion, where necessary, we append the subscripts "SL" and

"PL" (yielding $\vDash_{SL}$ and $\vDash_{PL}$) to indicate statement-logical and predicate-logical truth, respectively.

Let us apply our definition by using it to evaluate the logical truth of the formula,

Example 3.28. $\bigwedge y(Fy \rightarrow \bigvee xFx)$

The proof of the logical truth of this formula proceeds as follows. In accordance with Definition 3.14, the truth of example 3.28 must be examined under all extensional interpretations with non-empty domains. Let an arbitrary extensional interpretation of 3.28, with an arbitrary domain D, be given. D is thus some arbitrary finite or infinite set. Let $E_F = \{x \in D \mid F_I x$ is true$\}$ be the extension of the extensionally interpreted predicate letter 'F', F_I. We can now distinguish two cases: either E_F is empty or it is not:

1. $E_F = \varnothing$ means that $F_I y$ is false for all $y \in D$. Under this condition, 3.28 must be true, because the antecedent of its embedded conditional is false.

2. $E_F \neq \varnothing$ means that there is at least one $x \in D$ such that $F_I x$ is true. Under this condition, 3.28 must be true, because the consequent of its embedded conditional is true.

Formula 3.28 is thus true under all extensional interpretations with non-empty domains and is therefore logically true. QED.

How might one stumble upon such a proof? In this case, the central distinction of cases is suggested by the embedded conditional, which guarantees the truth of the formula whenever its antecedent is true or its consequent false. We then proceed by isolating the conditions under which the antecedent is false and then considering those left over. This is particularly easy to do for the present example, for the remaining cases clearly make the consequent of the embedded conditional true, hence the entire formula.

∗*Exercise 3.10.* Prove the logical truth of the following PL formulas:

1. $\wedge z\,(Pz \vee \neg Pz)$
2. $\wedge xFx \rightarrow \vee yFy$
3. $\wedge x(Tx \rightarrow Hx) \wedge Ts \rightarrow Hs$
4. $\neg \wedge x(Sx) \leftrightarrow \vee x(\neg Sx)$

b. The Relationship to Statement Logic

One question remains to be asked regarding the relationship between statement and predicate logic: what is the order of dependence between their respective conceptions of logical truth? In one direction, at least, the dependence is clear: there is no reason to expect a PL-truth to be SL-true. We need only consider example 3.25, "Every natural number is either prime or not prime." While SL-tautologies result from particular combinations of constituent statements joined by extensional connectives, typical PL-truths like 3.25 result from logical structures beyond the scope of SL analysis. The existence of such structures, to which, despite their logical interest, statement logic had remained blind, was one of the motives cited at the very beginning of this chapter for moving beyond statement logic in the first place. But how about the reverse direction? Is any SL-truth automatically a PL-truth? The answer is yes.

To see this, consider some arbitrary SL-truth S. By definition, S must have at least one tautologous SF. In order to perform a *predicate-logical* analysis of S, we must first identify all of its extensionally joined constituent statements, then analyze each of these by means of quantifiers, individual variables and constants, predicates, and a domain. Now consider the most fine-grained of S's SFs, the SF in which none of the connectives joining S's constituent statements has been abstracted away (see section II.2.2.b). It is an SF containing sentential letters $p_1, p_2, \ldots p_n$. According to the corollary to the Substitution Theorem, this formula, too, is tautologous (see section II.2.2.b). A PF of S differs from the most fine-grained SF of S only in that wherever the latter contains sentential letters $p_1, p_2, \ldots p_n$, the former contains PL formulas $P_1, P_2, \ldots P_n$. Because the PF can be seen to arise by substitution of PL formulas P_i in place of sentential letters p_i, we may safely apply the substitution theorem (see section II.2.2.b; the proof of the substitution theorem remains valid when PL formulas are substituted for sentential letters). Therefore, by the substitution theorem, this PF of S is logically true, and so S is PL-true.

The relationship between SL-truth and PL-truth outlined above also holds for other metalogical concepts. The reason for this is that just as the SL versions of these notions are defined in terms of SL-truth, so their PL analogues are defined in terms of PL-truth. It follows that whenever the SL version of a given metalogical concept applies, its PL counterpart does, too. However, if all I know is that the PL version applies, I am not entitled to claim anything about the SL counterpart.

c. The Entscheidungsproblem

Just as in statement logic, the definitions of the other metalogical notions of predicate logic are built on the prior definition of the logical truth of a formula. Determining the applicability or nonapplicability of this definition, or any other metalogical concept, thus reduces to determining whether or not a particular formula is assigned the value "true" by all extensional interpretations (in predicate logic, by all extensional interpretations with non-empty domains). In its general form, the problem of deciding whether or not a formula is logically true—that is, whether every permissible interpretation assigns it truth value T—is known as the *Entscheidungsproblem*, or "decision problem." The problem is still frequently referred to by its German name, which came into common currency after it was used by German mathematician David Hilbert (1862–1943) in a well-known lecture of 1900.

We have already solved the statement logic version of the decision problem by means of our procedure for determining, for any SL formula, whether or not it is SL-true. The procedure consists in the systematic examination of all possible extensional interpretations. Since we know at least one procedure (and there are other, more economical procedures) for deciding, in a finite number of steps, whether any arbitrary SL formula is logically true, the decision problem has been solved for statement logic.

But the situation is dramatically different in predicate logic, in which the decision problem *has no general solution.* The following theorem was proved by American logician Alonzo Church (1903–95) and British mathematician Alan Turing (1912–54):

> *Theorem:* There is no (mechanical) procedure by which we may decide, for any arbitrary PL formula, whether or not it is logically true.

The proof of this theorem lies outside the chosen scope of this book, but it may be found in many standard textbooks of classical predicate logic. Three further remarks on the theorem are in order, so as to make it clear just what it shows.

1. The theorem should *not* be understood as claiming merely that no mechanical procedure for deciding, in a finite number of steps, the logical truth of any arbitrary PL formula *has yet been found.* The claim is rather that no such procedure is *possible even in principle.* Needless to say, this assertion must be (and has been) proven.

2. The theorem does not rule out the possibility of discovering decision procedures that work for *special classes* of formulas. For example, there is a decision procedure for PL formulas containing only one-place predicates. All the theorem has to say about such partially successful procedures is that there will always be PL formulas, for which they fail to furnish any decision.

3. Nor does the theorem assert that there are formulas for which there is no fact of the matter as to whether or not they are logical truths—formulas that would be neither logically true nor not logically true, but something else. All the theorem claims is that there is no universally applicable procedure that will force a decision in all cases. It is thus a statement about the in-principle limitations of our ability to ascertain factual logical truth or its absence by mechanical means.

The fact that the general decision problem for predicate logic has no solution in no way prevents us from determining the logical truth of some formulas with relative ease. Our earlier proof of the logical truth of Example 3.28 (previous section) illustrates this point.

2.3. Logical Falsehood

With regard to logical falsehood, predicate logic offers no revolutionary innovations over statement logic. We thus move directly to the definition:

Definition 3.15.

1. A PF or PL formula is called a "(predicate-)logical falsehood" or "(predicate-)logically false" or a "contradiction" or "contradictory" just in case it is false under all extensional interpretations with non-empty domains.

2. A statement is called a "(predicate-)logical falsehood" or "(predicate-)logically false" or a "contradiction" or "contradictory" just in case it has at least one logically false PF.

My earlier remarks on the notions of logical truth and falsehood in statement logic apply equally well to predicate logic.

2.4. Valid Inference

a. Adequacy Criteria

As before, our criteria for the adequacy of a definition of valid inference will be extracted from our treatment of an example.

Example 3.29.   All teachers are helpful.

Ms. Smith is a teacher.

*

Therefore,   Ms. Smith is helpful.

Obviously, the validity of this inference turns on the repetition of particular expressions: 'teacher', 'Ms. Smith', and 'helpful'. This leads us to our first adequacy criterion:

Criterion 1: The validity of an inference depends on the repeated occurrence of predicates (ranging over a single domain) and possibly individual constants (also drawn from the same domain).

When predicates, or individual constants, are found to be drawn from different domains, we must first perform the appropriate domain expansion, bringing our case in line with single-sorted predicate logic (compare section III.1.1.d, Point 9).

As we have seen going back to our introduction (section I.1, Examples 1.4 and 1.5), any quantifiers and connectives we encounter are also relevant to validity:

Criterion 2: The validity of an inference depends on the quantifiers and connectives occurring in it.

Some aspects of the component statements of an inference are irrelevant to the validity of the inference, such as the meanings of the expressions 'teacher', 'Ms. Smith', and 'helpful'. Nor does the particular domain over which the bound variables range play any role. With regard to the validity of our inference, it does not matter whether there are three teachers in the world, or a hundred thousand, or infinitely many.

Criterion 3: The validity of an inference is independent of the meanings of predicates and individual constants occurring in it and of the (number and kind of elements in the) domain.

Finally, the validity of an inference demands truth transfer:

Criterion 4: The validity of an inference demands truth transfer; in other words, true premises may never coincide with a false conclusion.

Note that I have retained our old Criterion 4 rather than moving to 4* (see section II.2.4.f). My choice leads us to classical predicate logic. As in classical statement logic, the resulting theory is relatively simple, although its conception of valid inference may not be fully adequate, given the so-called paradoxes of implication.

b. Definition

By the same reasoning undertaken in section II.2.4.d, the four criteria lead us to the following definition of predicate-logically-valid inference:

Definition 3.16.

1. The inference from one PL formula *A* to a second, *B*, is said to be "(predicate-logically) valid" just in case *A*→*B* is a PL-truth.

2. The inference from a set of premises to a conclusion is said to be "(predicate-)logically valid" just in case "Conjunction of premises→Conclusion" is a PL-truth.

The symbolic notation for PL-valid inference is the same as that for SL-valid inference, $A \vDash B$.

The two parts of this definition, like their counterparts in statement logic, may be drawn together to form a unitary definition for both statements and PL formulas. We must be careful not to forget that the logical truth of *A*→*B* has different meaning depending on whether *A* and *B* are statements or PL formulas.

Definition 3.16'. Let *A* and *B* be statements or PL formulas. The inference from *A* to *B* is called "predicate-logically valid" just in case *A*→*B* is a PL-truth.

In the following sections, as in the corresponding sections of chapter 2, I will move directly to the more compact, one-part definitions of various metalogical notions.

First, however, let us apply Definition 3.16 (or 3.16) to our lead-off example:

Example 3.29. All teachers are helpful.

Ms. Smith is a teacher.

∗

Therefore,   Ms. Smith is helpful.

In accordance with Definition 3.16, we must now investigate the logical truth of the following statement:

Example 3.29a. All teachers are helpful ∧ Ms. Smith is a teacher →
Ms. Smith is helpful.

The PF of this statement that retains those elements relevant to the validity of the inference is clearly the following:

Example 3.29b. $\bigwedge x(Tx{\rightarrow}Hx){\wedge}Ts{\rightarrow}Hs$

Provided the PF 3.29b really does justice to the logically relevant elements of 3.29, demonstrating the applicability of Definition 3.16 to Example 3.29 boils down to showing that 3.29b is logically true. Fortunately, we have already accomplished this task in solving Exercise 3.10.3. Readers who are not satisfied with their own proofs are urged to consult appendix 2.

Up to now, our proofs of the logical truth of PL formulas have been rather tedious affairs. There are procedures for making such proofs more systematic, hence simpler. These methods lie outside the scope of this book, and so I will not consider them here. Interested readers are directed to the rich literature in mathematical logic, in which all such techniques are attacked with great enthusiasm. Our proofs, however, should be enough to reveal the intimate nature of the relationship between predicate logic and set theory. This relationship will not concern us further in the present chapter, though it plays a central role in the mathematical treatment of predicate logic.

2.5. Logical Equivalence

a. Definition

We begin with the following illustration of predicate-logical equivalence:

Example 3.30.   a. It is not the case that all logicians were cheerleaders in school.

b. There is at least one logician who was not a cheerleader in school.

With a little thought, it is easy to see that both statements make the same assertion. But they are neither SL-equivalent (their only SFs are '$\neg p$' or 'q' for the first statement, 'r' for the second), nor do they share any PFs, as the following analysis reveals:

    Example 3.30a.   a. $\neg \wedge x Sx$

                     b. $\vee x(\neg Sx)$

Nonetheless, it can be shown that both formulas have the same truth value under all possible interpretations (or, alternatively, that the biconditional formed out of them is true under all interpretations). And just as in statement logic, this is the touchstone of our definition of logical equivalence.

    Definition 3.17. Let *A* and *B* be statements or PL formulas. *A* and *B* are said to be *predicate-logically equivalent* just in case $A \leftrightarrow B$ is a PL-truth.

Nor should we be at all surprised to discover that predicate logic retains the same symbolic notation for logical equivalence employed in statement logic: $A \equiv B$.

b. Important Predicate-Logical Equivalences

The following four PL-equivalences, like their SL counterparts, are useful in simplifying formulas. For their proofs, I must once again defer to the relevant standard literature in mathematical logic.

    The first two equivalences are the predicate logic analogues of De Morgan's Laws:

$$\neg \vee x Fx \equiv \wedge x \neg Fx$$
$$\neg \wedge x Fx \equiv \vee x \neg Fx$$

Under certain circumstances, the second pair of equivalences allows us to distribute quantifiers over connectives, or to "factor" quantifiers:

$$\wedge x(Fx \wedge Gx) \equiv \wedge x Fx \wedge \wedge x Gx$$
$$\vee x(Fx \vee Gx) \equiv \vee x Fx \vee \vee x Gx$$

2.6. Further Metalogical Concepts

The definitions of any remaining metalogical notions of predicate logic may be formed by strict imitation of definitions for statement logic. This poses so few challenges, dear reader, that I have no reservations about assigning it as an exercise. My supplementary remarks in the metalogical section of the previous chapter apply equally well to predicate logic.

> *✳Exercise 3.11.* Form the predicate-logical definitions of the following meta-logical relations by analogy to the corresponding definitions in statement logic, taking *A* and *B* as either statements or PL formulas.
>
> 1. *A* and *B* are predicate-logically contrary.
> 2. *A* and *B* are predicate-logically contradictory.
> 3. *A* and *B* are predicate-logically consistent.
> 4. *A* and *B* are predicate-logically dependent.
> 5. *A* is predicate-logically necessary for *B*.
> 6. *A* is predicate-logically sufficient for *B*.

3. Review and Overview

This review and overview can safely be kept brief, as most of the reflections proffered in the corresponding section of chapter 2 (section II.2.3) may be imported wholesale into predicate logic. In particular, we will want to import our ruminations concerning the constitutive role played by examples in statement logic and our debunking of the problematic expectation that statement logic itself could justify all statement-logical inferences.

The most substantive difference between statement logic and predicate logic concerns the *Entscheidungsproblem,* a problem which though trivially solvable for statement logic has no general solution for predicate logic (see section III.2.2.c). This rather unfortunate state of affairs is somewhat mitigated by the mathematical approach to predicate logic, as alluded to in section IV.6.

4 ✳ The Mathematical Approach to Statement Logic

In the present chapter, we will take a second stab at statement logic, going right back to the drawing board. We will have to forget everything we have learned about statement logic so far, at least to the extent of not allowing ourselves to make use of any prior knowledge in *justifying* the claims we are about to make. Our prior knowledge of statement logic will, however, play an important role in *motivating* our investigation. This role is best understood as follows. In our earlier treatment of statement logic, we learned to understand the reasoning behind our definitions of particular concepts, along with certain proofs involving those concepts. But within the branch of mathematics to which we now turn, mathematical logic, there are no persuasive grounds (read: mathematical proofs) in support of these same definitions, nor are there compelling reasons for undertaking these proofs. But of course this does not make the definitions and proofs in question wholly arbitrary. We must rather understand them as having been motivated by our particular epistemic goals.

Before we turn to the mathematical approach, a few overarching remarks on the general characteristics of a mathematical approach to any subject matter are called for. These characteristics will make it clear why the mathematical treatment of logic is so appealing.

1. On Mathematical Approaches in General

In general, the mathematical approach to any subject matter is character-ized by three features: a tendency toward abstraction, a tendency toward axiomatization, and the obligation to provide airtight proofs of any prof-fered claims.

The mathematical *tendency toward abstraction* is revealed by the at-tempt to rigorously focus our attention on what, in some particular con-text, is thought to be "essential," the heart of the matter. This core is fre-quently "structural," consisting in the particular relations holding among objects. The assumption underlying this tendency is that its pursuit will reveal the relationships between the various attributes of objects in the clearest light possible. This general characterization may not strike those with little mathematical background as particularly informative. Nor should it; it can only really be understood by reference to concrete exam-ples. In any case, focusing on the essential always involves massive ab-straction, the elimination of all other attributes of the objects in question. The objects that remain, suitable as they are for mathematical treatment, are often fiercely abstract. Carrying out such abstraction requires, of course, that we know *which* attributes of the objects under scrutiny are es-sential in a given context. For objects of inquiry to be subjected to mathe-matical treatment, we must thus know a fair bit about them. In the present case, the mathematical treatment of statement logic, the requisite prior knowledge was gained over the course of chapter 2. In particular, we now know that the logical features of statements, and of the relations between statements, depend exclusively on logical forms. Accordingly, from the outset, the mathematical approach to statement logic will be concerned only with SFs, all other aspects having already been abstracted away. Our attention is directed squarely at that which determines the logical attrib-utes of statements; we are blind to everything else, no matter how interest-ing it might be in some other context.

Such abstraction has two further advantages, in addition to focusing our attention on the essential. First, it frequently allows us to discover commonalities between fields that were formerly thought to be fundamentally different. Such discoveries are a prized achievement of mathematical progress, for when an abstract description succeeds in showing that otherwise disparate fields share an underlying structural similarity, the methods of one may then be applied to the other. Second, the mathematical treatment of a subject causes many of its problems to drop away. For instance, the mathematical approach to logic need not bother itself with the storied problem of explaining what a statement actually *is* (compare section I.3.1). Of course this does not mean the problem has been *solved,* only that it poses no obstacle to addressing other questions from within the mathematical approach. Such bracketed problems return immediately once we leave the purely mathematical approach in an attempt to apply its results.

The second characteristic tendency of mathematics is *axiomatization.* To a first approximation, axiomatization consists in bringing order to the set of statements held true within a given field. Toward this end, a small subset of these statements is sought, as small as possible, such that all of the other statements follow as logical consequences. The statements in this small subset, the *axioms,* thus entail the sum total of all knowledge in the field in question. All the true statements about the subject of the field in question may thus be classified as belonging either to the class of axioms, or to the class of *theorems,* each member of which is derived, or proven, on the basis of the axioms (the sorting of statements into one of the two classes need not always be unambiguous). The axioms themselves cannot, of course, be proven, since proof itself consists in derivation from the axioms. At one time mathematicians hoped for some sort of direct insight into the truth of the axioms. Within mathematics, the current consensus is that one ought not even to ask after the *truth* of axioms (though one must ask after their consistency). The interesting question is, rather, what theorems can be derived from a particular set of axioms, taking the axioms as given? Mathematical statements thus become essentially conditional: *if* such and such axioms hold, *then* so do the following theorems. Accordingly, the question as to *whether* and in what sense the axioms actually *do* hold is entirely excluded from mathematics itself. Needless to say, mathematicians are unlikely to investigate simply *any* system of axioms. Their attention is rather confined to those that, for one reason or another, seem interesting, where such reasons can be highly variable. Indeed, mathematicians have been known to disagree about which axiom systems are of interest, but disputes of this sort are not, fundamentally, *mathematical.* The axiomatic representation of a field promises to furnish three sorts of contribution: an economical representation of the state of knowledge in a given field; an account of the relations of dependence among the statements of the field; and, finally, a clear determination of the standards of justification to which anyone wishing to make claims within the given field will be held responsible.

A third characteristic of mathematics is that it demands *airtight proofs* for all assertions. This characteristic is intimately connected with the tendency toward axiomatization, as discussed above. Only within an axiomatic system is it entirely clear what presuppositions a proof may take as its starting points. If, in addition, there is also an explicit account of the rules of inference acceptable in proof—and although this is typically not the case in mathematics, it is rarely a point of controversy—then every step in a given proof can likewise be made explicit. It should be noted, however, that within mathematics, conceptions of airtight proof are subject to historical evolution. Nor is this particularly surprising, given that even in mathematics it is impossible to define *all* terms, since every definition itself may reference terms other than those being defined. Consequently, a concept fully accepted in one era as primitive and undefined may, in some later era, given new discoveries, find itself subject to the demand for explicit definition (by reference to *other* concepts lacking explicit definitions). So while put abstractly, the demand for airtight proofs appears to be a universal, ahistorical characteristic of mathematics, conceptions of what counts as an airtight proof are susceptible to historical change.

So much for mathematical treatments in general. With regard to the mathematical treatment of statement logic, there are two complementary approaches, model theory and proof theory, both of which are built on the syntactic analysis of SFs (any unfamiliar expressions will be explained below, in the appropriate sections). Over the course of these sections we will see, concretely, how the three tendencies sketched above express themselves. Model theory draws most heavily on the procedure invoked in chapter 2, in our development of statement logic. Proof theory, by contrast, involves the axiomatization of logical truths. An explanation of the motives behind these two approaches will have to wait until later. Before we begin, one further preparatory remark is called for. This chapter in no way aspires toward a complete presentation of the sort of mathematical approach that may be found in numerous textbooks on mathematical logic. Nor will I be striving to achieve the benchmark mathematical level of precision. My aim is rather to present and explain the basic ideas at work in the mathematical approach to logic. Rather than performing proofs of most of the theorems, I will frequently defer to the relevant literature. I do, however, hope to clarify the contents of these theorems, together with their logical significance.

2. The Syntax of Statement Logic

In chapter 2, we arrived at SL formulas by way of the following itinerary: We began by introducing statements as sentences with definite truth value, after which we discussed the extensional connectives, made the transition to logical form, and finally represented these forms by means of a specially devised symbol system. In our subsequent employment of the final product of these four steps, SL formulas, our prior itinerary was often of little consequence. This was particularly true of the procedure whereby we eventually arrived at our definitions of logical truth and valid inference. Accordingly, we now reintroduce the notion of a statement-logical formula without explicit recourse to statements or their properties. Instead, following the tendency toward abstraction inherent in the mathematical approach, we abstract away everything that does not pertain to the SL formulas themselves, understood as bare typographical constructs. The abstraction is radical, leaving us with nothing but uninterpreted strings of symbols.

In logic, a symbol system for writing logical formulas is frequently called a *language*. Obviously we are not talking about languages like English or Turkish, but about *artificial, formal languages*. I will call the language of statement logic "L," invoking a standard convention. The permissible formulas of L will be introduced by means of a specification of L's repertoire of symbols, followed by the rules by which these symbols may be combined to form formulas. The symbols must be understood as having *no meaning;* in a sense, they are pure typography, mere figures or spots of ink on paper, drawn here or there at will, but meaning nothing, standing for nothing, and requiring no thought. Strictly speaking, the symbols are not even symbols, because mere spots of ink on paper have no symbolic significance. In what follows, however, I will continue to talk of them as symbols, if only because there is no better English word for such meaningless scratches. When a particular symbol appears in a particular place, the only fact of the matter is that it is *this* symbol that occupies this place, and not some other, or none at all, and no amount of reflection can reveal more.

The set of symbols in L may be divided into three groups. The first group consists in *variables* (also known as *sentential variables, atomic sentences, primitive sentences,* or *sentential letters*). The second contains *operators* (or *connectives, sentential connectives,* or *functors*), and the third is comprised of *auxiliary signs.* But such designations are already misleading. They make it sound as if the various symbols had different functions or different meanings, by which we classified them as belonging to the three groups. At this stage in our construction of statement logic, however, there are no such differences. The symbols to be introduced mean nothing. As of yet, they have no particular functions, and so there is no functional basis for making distinctions among them. They differ from each other only typographically. Armed with this warning, not to read anything into the symbols, we are ready to introduce them.

* The *variables* are the (countably infinite) set of letters $p_1, p_2, p_3, \ldots$, or $p, q, r \ldots$. It makes no difference whether we call them variables, sentential letters, atomic sentences, or anything else, because, once again, the letters have no meaning: they are either present or absent. In chapter 2, the situation was completely different. There I was at great pains to distinguish sentential letters from the abbreviations of statements, going so far as to use different letters (section II.1.2.b, Points 1 and 2, pp). Here, however, the letters mean nothing, and so we may call them what we will.

* The *operators* are symbols $\neg, \wedge, \vee, \rightarrow, \leftrightarrow$. For the present, these symbols are also meaningless, though they bear an uncanny resemblance to our familiar connectives. At this stage, we enjoy considerable freedom in our choice of operators. Our choice is driven by the fact that at a later stage, of course, we will want to identify them with the connectives of statement logic, thus ascribing them meaning. But we know from our earlier discussion of statement logic that because the connectives may be used to express each other, we do not really need all of them (see section II.2.5, Points 8 and 9). In this section and the one following it, I will help myself to all five of the operators above as part of L. In section IV.4, however, I will limit myself to $\neg$ and $\rightarrow$, thus simplifying several definitions.

* Finally, we will use two *auxiliary signs,* the parentheses, (and).

Once again, at this stage these symbols mean nothing; they are not even symbols. Right now, their only function is to be used in forming strings (understood as linear arrangements). In other words, they may be written down in any order, with any frequency, at any length. Examples of such strings include the following:

$\rightarrow pr) \vee \wedge p \neg$

or

$(p \wedge q) \vee r$

or

$)()()(ppp qqq \vee \vee \vee$

Now, in natural languages, not all arrangements of words (or letters) are meaningful. Syntax is understood as the study of the rules (or as the set of rules) that must be followed for a series of words to form a meaningful sentence. The mathematical approach to statement logic is not really interested in all possible strings of symbols (after all, somehow or another we want to end up with statement logic, as articulated in chapter 2). Accordingly, we now distinguish between *well-formed* and *ill-formed* strings of symbols, calling the rules whereby we distinguish strings of one sort from the other the *syntax* of the language under development. The well-formed strings of symbols will turn out to be just those that coincide, typographically, with familiar SL formulas. For this reason they are also known as the *formulas* of L or, sometimes, the *sentences* of L. Again, it does not matter what we call them; we must only understand that we are no longer dealing with wholly arbitrary strings of symbols but with strings that must be generated in accordance with particular rules. In the literature, such formulas are also referred to as "WFFs," for "well-formed formulas." The formulas of L, and hence the syntax of L, are defined by the following construction rules.

Definition 4.1.

1. The variables are formulas.
2. If P is a formula, ¬P is also a formula.
3. If P and Q are formulas, so are (P∧Q), (P∨Q), (P→Q), and (P↔Q).
4. No string of symbols is a formula unless it can be constructed in a finite number of applications of rules 1–3.

Please note that the letters P and Q in Definition 4.1 should not be confused with lowercase letters p and q. While the latter belong to language L, P and Q are merely placeholders for formulas of L. They *do not* belong to language L and are known as *metalanguage variables* (though nothing varies—they are simply placeholders).

It is quite clear that Definition 4.1 permits us to form a set of symbol strings that coincides typographically with the set of SL formulas. This set is a subset of the set of all possible strings composed of the symbols of L. Note that, by Rule 3, operators $\vee$, $\wedge$, $\rightarrow$, and $\leftrightarrow$ must always be used together with parentheses, and so while $(p \wedge q)$ is a formula, $p \wedge q$ is *not*. With recourse to our parenthesis convention, however, we will always omit the outermost pair of parentheses in writing any formula. We may also save parentheses by obeying the full parenthesis convention introduced in section II.1.2.b, Point 8. But such details need concern us no further here.

While at first blush this way of introducing formulas might strike us as somewhat pedantic, it must be understood in light of the drive toward airtight proofs, cited earlier as characteristic of the mathematical approach. This is because the demand for rules of construction of the sort provided in Definition 4.1 forces us to make all of the relevant properties of formulas explicit. This done, there can be no doubt, and no difference of opinion, as to which properties formulas possess. Henceforth all claims about formulas must be justified by recourse to these properties, and only these.

Within the mathematical approach to logic, every claim made about SL formulas, no matter how trivial or obvious it might seem, demands proof. For example, chapter 2 taught us that every nonatomic SL formula has a main connective, allowing us to classify it, by reference to this main connective, as a conjunction, disjunction, etc. (See section II.1.2.b). In that context, such claims were warranted by the fact that formulas arose by abstraction from statements. In the present chapter, of course, no such appeal to provenance is available to us. In mathematical logic, the following theorem on the unequivocal classification of formulas must be proven on the basis of Definition 4.1 alone.

> *Theorem 4.1:* Every formula is either a variable, or a negation, or a conjunction, or a disjunction, or a conditional, or a biconditional; furthermore, these cases are mutually exclusive.

Before attempting to prove this theorem, one would first have to define negation, conjunction, etc. Similarly, every other assertion about formulas also requires proof.

Our introduction of the syntax of L clearly exhibits the tendency toward abstraction so characteristic of mathematics (see section IV.1). In chapter 2, it took a long chain of reflections to arrive at our conception of SL formulas. In the end, those formulas were all well formed, because we had set out from meaningful statements, extracting formulas from them by abstraction (the transition to SF) and representation (the expression of SF by means of SL formula). If we were interested only in the formulas themselves and their properties, we would spare ourselves the long chain of reflections, choosing instead to define their syntax, as in Definition 4.1. But we should not forget that this definition was deliberately designed to define a set of formulas typographically identical with the SL formulas—though our original path toward the latter seemed to have nothing to do with mathematics.

Once the syntax of L—the rules for constructing SL formulas—has been established, logic may be pursued along two different, though complementary paths. In the end, our goal is to arrive at the concept of valid inference, and so it is time to go beyond uninterpreted strings of symbols. The first path, as sketched in the following section, will closely track the lessons of chapter 2.

3. Semantics: Model Theory

"Semantics" is ordinarily understood as a discipline concerned with the meanings of symbols. In logic, by contrast, semantics is generally thought of as the systematic statement of the conditions under which the sentences of a formal language are true or false. The connection between these two senses of "semantics" is as follows. When we know the meaning of a statement, we also know the circumstances under which the statement is true, provided the statement is sufficiently concrete and precise. These circumstances are known as the "truth conditions" of the statement. For example, anyone who understands the statement "Tomorrow is Christmas" also understands the condition under which this statement is true: provided it is uttered on December 24. The converse is also true: when we know the truth conditions of a statement, we know its meaning, or at least a significant part of it. If, for example, we know that a given statement is true if and only if the moon is made of green cheese, it is highly plausible that the statement asserts that the moon is made of green cheese. The intimate nature of the relationship between the meaning of a statement and its truth conditions justifies the use of the term "semantics" for the study of truth conditions.

The goal of the semantics of L is thus the specification of the truth conditions for the formulas of L. On first hearing, this sounds all wrong, for we learned in chapter 2 that formulas have no truth value; the property of being true or false is removed from statements over the course of their abstraction to SFs. So how could formulas have truth conditions? In the present context, in which formulas were introduced in purely syntactic terms in Definition 4.1, this reflection is entirely irrelevant; we are not entitled to any assumptions about the meanings of formulas. Our talk of the truth conditions of formulas hearkens back to our discussion of the truth analysis of extensionally interpreted formulas (section II.1.3.c). There we began by assigning a truth value to every sentential letter in a given formula, after which, consulting the truth tables for the connectives, we assigned truth values to successively larger subformulas and, finally, to the formula itself. The same procedure is open to model theory.

We first assign one of the two truth values to each variable of L. This is called an *allotment* (of truth values to the variables of L). Whereas the process of extensional interpretation only concerned itself with the few sentential letters in a given formula, we now assign truth values to *all* of the variables of L. But we abstract from any substantive assumptions about the *nature* of truth values themselves. As far as we are concerned, we are simply assigning one of the two letters T and F to each of the variables; we might just as well use 1 and 0 or apples and bananas. As we recall from chapter 2, truth analysis need never take the factual difference between truth and falsehood into account; all it requires are the truth tables for the connectives. Similarly, we have now abstracted away the meanings of "truth" and "falsehood," leaving only the fact of their difference. The notion of an allotment is defined as follows:

> **Definition 4.2.** The assignment of one truth value to each of the variables of L is called an *allotment* (of truth values to the variables) of L.

Having made an allotment, the next step is to extend it to provide an assignment of truth values to *all* the formulas of L. If this extension is to have anything to do with statement logic, it cannot be arbitrary. The operators $\neg$, $\vee$, $\wedge$, $\rightarrow$, and $\leftrightarrow$, so far introduced without a shred of meaning, are meant to function like the connectives of chapter 2, which were modeled on natural language. And so in concrete terms, we must assign truth values to the formulas of L, in accordance with the truth values already allotted to the sentential letters, in such a way as to respect the truth tables for the connectives. This sort of assignment of truth values to the formulas of L is called an *evaluation* (of the formulas) of L, defined as follows:

> **Definition 4.3.** Let an allotment of L be given. The assignment of one truth value to each of the formulas of L is called an *evaluation* of (the formulas of) L just in case the following conditions hold for any arbitrary formulas P and Q of L:

1. If *P* is a variable, it is assigned the same truth value as in the allotment;

2. ¬*P* is assigned the value *T* just in case *P* is assigned the value *F*;

3. (*P*∧*Q*) is assigned the value *T* just in case both *P* and *Q* are assigned the value *T*;

4. (*P*∨*Q*) is assigned the value *T* just in case either *P* or *Q* is assigned the value *T*;

5. (*P*→*Q*) is assigned the value *F* just in case *P* is assigned the value *T* and *Q* the value *F*;

6. (*P*↔*Q*) is assigned the value *T* just in case both *P* and *Q* are assigned the same truth value.

This definition may be understood as assigning truth values to the formulas of L step by step, retracing the steps of the syntax of L as set out in Definition 4.1, by which the formulas themselves are generated. Beginning with the variables, and proceeding, next, to formulas containing only two variables, the repeated application of Rules 2 through 6 assigns truth values to ever more complex formulas. The chief difference between the evaluation of L and our earlier notion of extensional interpretation consists in the fact that while the former assigns a truth value to *every* sentential letter and thus *every* formula of *S,* the latter confines itself to assigning truth values to the sentential letters and thus subformulas occurring in a particular formula.

Definition 4.3 articulates the *semantics* of language L in the sense of providing the conditions under which the formulas of L are true (or false). *Within the bounds of logic,* everything we need to know about the connectives is contained within their truth tables. Consequently, the mathematical approach to statement logic abstracts away all of their properties, leaving only the fact that they occur between or before formulas (Definition 4.1), and the way in which the truth value of a negation, or a formula joined by a binary connective, depends on the truth value of its constituent formula(s) (Definition 4.3).

Once again, we observe the tendency toward abstraction inherent in the mathematical approach, as described in section IV.1. Henceforth, any claims made in the mathematical development of statement logic, in which the properties of the connectives play a role, must rely exclusively on the properties set out in Definitions 4.1 and 4.3. No other substantive assumptions regarding the connectives may come into play. This, in turn, is a consequence of the mathematical demand for airtight proofs (section IV.1): any properties of the objects under study that are to feature in either assertions or their proofs must *first* be stipulated in the explicit definitions of these objects.

With a view toward our later introduction of the notion of logical truth, we are particularly interested in those evaluations that assign value T to a particular formula. They are important enough to deserve their own name:

> *Definition 4.4.* A *model* of formula P is an evaluation of L that assigns truth value T to P.

It is also sometimes said that the evaluations on which P is assigned truth value T *satisfy* P. The origins of these odd-sounding uses of "model" and "satisfaction" need not concern us here. In any case, we will shortly come to understand why the present approach to logic is known as "model theory." With the help of the concepts introduced so far, we are now in a position to reformulate our understanding of the notion of statement-logical truth, which we discussed in section II.2.2.a. The content of this notion remains the same.

> *Definition 4.5.* A given formula P of L is said to be "statement-logically true" just in case all of the evaluations of L are models of P (or, put differently, just in case P is satisfied by all of the evaluations of L).

Now we can see why the present mathematical approach to statement logic is called "model theory": it redefines the logically central concept of statement-logical truth in terms of the concept of a model. Again, this redefinition in no way modifies anything we learned in section II.2. The only difference is that this time we have set out from a place in which everything irrelevant to the manipulation of formulas has already been abstracted away.

I conclude this section on the model theoretic approach to statement logic with the model theoretic definition of valid inference. In essence, this definition is identical with the first part of Definition 2.11, though it is now formulated more along the lines familiar from textbooks in mathematical logic.

> *Definition 4.6.* The inference from formulas $P_1, \ldots P_n$ to formula Q is said to be "statement-logically valid," just in case every model of $P_1, \ldots P_n$ is also a model of Q.

Where Definition 2.11 assumes a single premise, 4.6 allows an entire set; but of course premises $P_1, \ldots P_n$ can easily be combined, by conjunction, to form a single premise $P = P_1 \wedge \ldots \wedge P_n$. On the surface, 4.6 appears not to require the logical truth of the conditional formed by premises and conclusion, as demanded by 2.11, but the condition stated in 4.6 is equivalent. For if every model of P is also a model of Q, $P \rightarrow Q$ must be logically true, since on every interpretation on which P is true, Q is also true, while on every interpretation on which P is false, the conditional is automatically true. Conversely, if $P \rightarrow Q$ is logically true, there are no interpretations on which P is true and Q false, so every model of P is also a model of Q.

There is no need to reduce the other metalogical notions discussed in section II.2 to the present conception of statement-logical truth. In every case, the relevant definitions can be imported word for word.

4. Proof Theory

In the model-theoretic approach to statement logic pursued so far, we have made use of one important aspect of the meanings of the connectives in arriving at our definitions of statement-logical truth and validity: their truth tables. The present proof-theoretic venture takes the mathematical tendency toward abstraction even further, presenting definitions of meta-logical notions in which even the meanings of the connectives have receded entirely. In other words, we will be following a purely syntactic procedure. When it comes time to discuss certain laws for constructing formulas, we will do so without considering the meanings, or special functions, of any of their constituent symbols. Furthermore, the proof-theoretic approach exhibits a particularly vigorous strain of the typically mathematical axiomatic tendency.

The basic idea to be explored here is the proposal that all strings of symbols typographically congruent with SL-true formulas can be generated in accordance with purely syntactic formation laws. These formation laws are given by a series of *axioms* and (one or more) *inference rules* (or *deduction rules*). Applied to the axioms, the inference rules license the generation of the entire set of formulas in which we are interested. This method, applied to statement logic, yields what is known as a *calculus of statement logic* (or *sentential calculus*). The Latin *calculus* originally meant "reckoning stone," a stone token whose systematic placement aided in the mechanical performance of arithmetic operations. Similarly, in the present calculus, symbols are manipulated—written down in sequence, erased, rearranged, etc.—in accordance with the aforementioned rules. A calculus in this sense is nothing more than a system for the production of typographic shapes, just as the rules of chess can be seen as a system for the production of legal board configurations. The expressions with which we begin, and the rules whereby we manipulate them, are so chosen as to ensure that the manipulations we perform will generate the desired class of expressions. The calculus of statement logic thus begins with a small number of axiomatic formulas, typographically identical with logical truths, and a set of rules whereby further formulas may be generated out of them, which for their part are also typographically congruent with logical truths. The end result is known as an *uninterpreted formal system*.

Before embarking on the construction of this system, it is worth asking what the *point* of such a logical calculus is. Are we perhaps simply blindly following the current of mathematical tendencies, tendencies which, while they might be fruitful enough in mathematics, in no way further our understanding of logic? Nothing could be further from the truth. To be sure, *in one sense,* statement logic itself has no need of a calculus. We already have a procedure in hand for deciding, for any SL formula, whether or not it is SL-true. The method of truth analysis sketched in section II.1.3c is one such procedure, and other decision tools, some of them more efficient, are also available. Under these conditions, the only plausible motive for developing a calculus of statement logic would appear to be the clerical zest for tidiness, whose obsessive demands are satisfied by nothing less than the orderly arrangement of all SL-truths. However, the study of the calculus of statement logic serves as a particularly accessible point of entry into a method that acquires much greater significance in other branches of logic, including predicate logic, in which there *are no* decision procedures (see section II.2.2.c). In the absence of an effective procedure for assessing logical truth, their syntactic characterization is particularly welcome.

There is one further practical reason, in addition to its didactic utility in preparing us for other branches of logic, for pursing the calculus of statement logic. Whenever we find ourselves dissatisfied with a given theory, we seek to improve it. Toward this end, it is advantageous to have different representations of the theory at our disposal. Where one representation is best suited to revealing the effects of one modification, other representations will display the consequences of other proposed improvements. Axiomatic representations of theories are particularly suited to revealing the effects of suggested modifications, because they compress the entire content of the theory in question into a few axioms. And so, in the present case, we find that when modifications to classical statement logic are proposed in response to the so-called paradoxes of implication (see section II.2.4.f), they are usually targeted at the calculus of statement logic.

The calculus of statement logic can take many different forms; there are many different arrangements of axioms and inference rules that lead to the same result. Such calculi often differ, first, on which operators (connectives) they employ. The more operators allowed, the more axioms are needed. On the other hand, employing fewer operators means that otherwise familiar formulas take on unfamiliar forms. This consequence is particularly evident when we restrict ourselves to the use of the Sheffer Stroke (compare section II.2.5.c, Point 9). Since our concern here is with the basics, it is best to develop a fairly clear-cut calculus. Toward this end, our only operators will be $\neg$ and $\rightarrow$. As shown in section II.2.5.c, Point 8, these two extensional connectives may be used to express all of the others; in the terms introduced in that section, $\neg$ and $\rightarrow$ form a *functionally complete* system of connectives. And so, in place of Definition 4.1, in which the conjunction, disjunction, and biconditional were permitted in the construction of well-formed formulas, we invoke the following reduced syntax:

Definition 4.7.
　　1. The variables are formulas.
　　2. If P is a formula, so is $\neg P$.
　　3. If P and Q are formulas, so is $(P \rightarrow Q)$.
　　4. No string of symbols is a formula unless it can be constructed in a finite number of applications of rules 1–3.

The permissible formulas of our calculus thus contain only variables, the operators $\neg$ and $\rightarrow$, and parentheses. The calculus specifies particular formulas as axioms and provides a rule for proceeding from given formulas to new formulas. Strictly speaking, the calculus actually sets out not from particular formulas but from *formula schemata,* which contain placeholders for formulas. A formula schema becomes an actual formula when every occurrence of its placeholders is replaced by the same formulas. Our axioms are really *axiom schemata.* Here, then, is the definition of our calculus C. For the moment, C is nothing more than a recipe for the construction of a particular set of formulas. We will return to consider the statement-logical interest of this set later.

> *Definition 4.8.* For all formulas P, Q, and R, the following formulas are axioms of calculus C:
>   1. $P \rightarrow (Q \rightarrow P)$
>   2. $(P \rightarrow (Q \rightarrow R)) \rightarrow ((P \rightarrow Q) \rightarrow (P \rightarrow R))$
>   3. $(\neg P \rightarrow \neg Q) \rightarrow (Q \rightarrow P)$

The deduction rule D is as follows:

> D: Given P and $P \rightarrow Q$, we may write down Q.

Strictly speaking, C has an infinite number of formulas as axioms. For example, the first axiom of 4.8 yields the formula $p \rightarrow (q \rightarrow p)$ when p and q are substituted for P and Q, respectively, but it also yields the formula $\neg p \rightarrow (\neg q \rightarrow \neg p)$ when $\neg p$ and $\neg q$ are substituted for P and Q, and so on. Within the calculus itself, none of the symbols, including the operators $\neg$ and $\rightarrow$, has the slightest meaning. All that matters is that these two symbols are different from one another, and from the letters that stand for formulas. Instead of the symbols used here, we might just as well use apples, pears, oranges, nuts, etc. The very same calculus would then begin by stipulating which strings of apples, pears, oranges, nuts, etc. could be presupposed and which new strings generated from them. Nor would the applehood of the apples or the pearness of the pears matter to this procedure, either. Definition 4.8 is analogous to the definitions of the formulas themselves in Definitions 4.1 and 4.7 in the sense of distinguishing, on purely syntactic grounds, the class of formulas from the prior, larger class of symbol strings to which it belongs.

With calculus C in place, we are now in a position to define *(formal) provability* (in C); this, after all, was what C was built for. Later on we will show that this conception of provability corresponds to the familiar notion of statement-logical truth, and consider the *nature* of the correspondence. "Provable in C" applies only to the axioms of C, together with those formulas that arise out of the axioms by repeated application of the deduction rule D. More precisely,

> *Definition 4.9.* *(Formally) provable formulas in* C:
> 1. The axioms of C are provable in C.
> 2. All of the formulas that result from the repeated application of deduction rule D to formulas provable in C are also provable in C.
> 3. Only those formulas satisfying Conditions 1 and 2 are provable in C.

In other words, all and only the formulas generated by calculus C are considered (formally) provable in C. This is precisely what provability in C amounts to: that just these formulas, and no others, may be generated within C. It is therefore inappropriate to project any associations the word "provable" might otherwise have onto our understanding of (formal) provability in C, as stipulated by Definition 4.9. Symbolically, we will represent provability in C by '$\vdash_C$' and when it is clear which calculus we have in mind, we omit the subscript 'C'. The similarity between the provability sign, '$\vdash$', and the sign for logical truth, '$\vDash$', is no coincidence; as we will shortly see, the two notions have a great deal to do with one another.

We now illustrate the workings of a proof in C by considering a simple example, in which a desired formula is generated in accordance with Definition 4.9. We will show that $(p{\rightarrow}p)$ is provable, or $\vdash(p{\rightarrow}p)$. Beginning with the first axiom schema in 4.8, we substitute variable p for P, and formula $q{\rightarrow}p$ for Q. In accordance with Point 1 of Definition 4.9, the resulting formula is provable:

(1) $\vdash p{\rightarrow}((q{\rightarrow}p){\rightarrow}p)$

Next we turn to the second axiom schema of 4.8, substituting variable p for P, formula q→p for Q, and variable p for R. Once again, by Point 1 of Definition 4.9,

(2) $\vdash (p{\rightarrow}((q{\rightarrow}p){\rightarrow}p)){\rightarrow}((p{\rightarrow}(q{\rightarrow}p)){\rightarrow}(p{\rightarrow}p))$

We are now in a position to apply the deduction rule D to (1) and (2), since (1) consists in the antecedent of the conditional (2). Therefore, by D,

$$(3) \vdash (p{\rightarrow}(q{\rightarrow}p)){\rightarrow}(p{\rightarrow}p)$$

Revisiting the first axiom of Definition 4.8, we substitute variable p for P and variable q for Q:

$$(4) \vdash p{\rightarrow}(q{\rightarrow}p)$$

Finally, recognizing that (4) is the antecedent of conditional (3), we apply D again, yielding,

$$(5) \vdash p{\rightarrow}p$$

This shows that $p{\rightarrow}p$ is provable in C.

We now require the notion of *(formal) derivability in* C, which will later turn out to correspond to that of statement-logical validity. The main idea involves taking formulas $A_1, A_2, \ldots A_n$ as additional axioms of C and asking whether a given formula B is provable in this new, expanded calculus. Formulas $A_1, A_2, \ldots A_n$ are known as *premises*. The definition of derivability in C is as follows.

> *Definition 4.10:* A formula B is said to be (formally) derivable in C from formulas $A_1, A_2, \ldots A_n$ just in case B is provable in the calculus that results from expanding C by the addition of premises $A_1, A_2, \ldots A_n$ as axioms.

The symbol '$\vdash_C$' will also be used to express derivability in C, omitting the subscript whenever it is clear which calculus we have in mind. So "B is derivable from $A_1, A_2, \ldots A_n$" may also be written as, "$A_1, A_2, \ldots A_n \vdash B$."

As a simple example, let us attempt a derivation of the so-called chain rule:

$$p{\rightarrow}q, \; q{\rightarrow}r \vdash p{\rightarrow}r$$

The formal derivation proceeds as follows. We begin by adding the two premises to our calculus. Once added, the premises are provable:

(1) $\vdash p \to q$

(2) $\vdash q \to r$

In the second axiom schema of 4.8, we substitute p for P, q for Q, and r for R, yielding,

(3) $\vdash (p \to (q \to r)) \to ((p \to q) \to (p \to r))$

By the first axiom schema of 4.8, substituting $(q \to r)$ for P and p for Q, we obtain,

(4) $\vdash (q \to r) \to (p \to (q \to r))$

Next we apply the deduction rule D to (2) and (4):

(5) $\vdash p \to (q \to r)$

And then again to (5) and (3):

(6) $\vdash (p \to q) \to (p \to r)$

Finally, we apply D to (1) and (6), yielding the desired result:

(7) $\vdash (p \to r)$

Further tools for working with calculi are furnished by so-called metatheorems. A metatheorem, as the name suggests, is a theorem *about* a calculus, whereas proofs or derivations are always carried out *within* a given calculus. Typical metatheorems have something like the following form: If formulas of *this* type are provable in C, then formulas of *that* type are also provable in C. Alternatively, a metatheorem might claim, if *this* derivability relation holds in C, so does *that* derivability relation. Whenever we speak of the properties of a calculus, or relations that hold within it, we are invoking a metatheorem. One of the most productive metatheorems, and consequently one of the most important of them, is called the deduction theorem. It reads as follows:

> **Theorem 4.2.**   If $A_1, A_2, \ldots A_n \vdash B$,
>
>   then $A_1, A_2, \ldots A_{n-1} \vdash A_n \rightarrow B$

Or in other words, if a formula B is derivable from premises $A_1, A_2, \ldots A_n$, then formula $A_n \rightarrow B$ is derivable from premises $A_1, A_2, \ldots A_{n-1}$. I defer to the standard texts in mathematical logic for discussions of the proof of this theorem and its applications.

But now, at long last, we are owed an account of what, exactly, this calculus C has to do with statement logic. In fact, as of this point, it has almost nothing to do with statement logic, except for the fact that the structures manipulated within C bear a "coincidental" resemblance to SL formulas. In a sense, the resemblance really is coincidental, since we might easily have lined up nuts in place of the various sentential letters, an apple in place of the $\neg$, an orange in place of the $\rightarrow$, and bananas in place of the parentheses. If we had, our results would not have borne much in the way of typographical similarity to SL formulas. It would never have occurred to anyone that the fruit-strings generated in accordance with C, which, by the way, we might have arranged vertically, had the slightest connection to statement logic. But once we *interpret* the letters p, q, etc. as sentential letters, the $\neg$ as the negation, the $\rightarrow$ as the conditional, and symbols (and) as parentheses, calculus C may be seen to reveal the "provability" of certain SL formulas. Furthermore, C may also be seen to underwrite a "derivability" relation between SL formulas $A_1, A_2, \ldots A_n$ and B. As to what provability and derivability actually amount to, once the symbol strings of C are interpreted *as SL formulas,* is not yet entirely clear. At present, all we have learned is the mechanical generation of formulas out of other formulas in accordance with Definitions 4.6 and 4.7.

The link between C and statement logic is forged by two mutually complementary theorems, both of which demand proof. The first theorem asserts that the derivability (in C) of one formula from others entails the corresponding relation of statement-logically valid inference. This attribute of C is known as *soundness*. C is sound in the sense that derivability in C implies logical consequence, once the formulas of C are interpreted as SL formulas. Expressed by means of the symbols that I introduced earlier, the soundness theorem is as follows:

> **Theorem 4.3.**   The soundness of C
>
> If $A_1, A_2, \ldots A_n \vdash B,$
>
> then $A_1, A_2, \ldots A_n \vDash B.$

The same relationship holds between provability and SL-truth, that is, in the special case in which there are no premises $A_1, A_2, \ldots A_n,$

> If $\vdash B$, then $\vDash B.$

I will not prove Theorem 4.3 (though such proof is clearly called for), contenting myself instead with a proof of the more restricted claim that provable formulas of L, interpreted as SL formulas, are SL-true; we will show that if $\vdash B$, then $\vDash B$. The first step is to show that the axioms of C, interpreted as SL formulas, are SL-true. Toward this end, we insert variables p, q, and r in place of P, Q, and R, in all of the axiom schemata of Definition 4.8. It is then easy to show, by means of truth tables, that the resulting formulas, $p \rightarrow (q \rightarrow p)$, $(p \rightarrow (q \rightarrow r)) \rightarrow ((p \rightarrow q) \rightarrow (p \rightarrow r))$ and $(\neg p \rightarrow \neg q) \rightarrow (q \rightarrow p)$, are all SL-true. By the Substitution Theorem (section II.2.2.b), any formula that fits one of the axiom schemata of Definition 4.8 is also an SL-truth. Furthermore, the deduction rule in Definition 4.8 is clearly a valid inference form, namely modus ponens (see section II.2.4.e, Point 6). If the premise of a valid inference is SL-true, the conclusion is, too. So calculus C generates only SL-true formulas.

The second theorem expresses the converse of the first, as its formal statement makes clear. It asserts that *all* relations of statement-logically valid inference are captured by calculus C. This feature of C is known as *completeness.* In symbolic terms,

Theorem 4.4.   The completeness of C

If $A_1, A_2, \ldots A_n \vDash B,$

then $A_1, A_2, \ldots A_n \vdash B.$

Again, this relationship also holds when we omit premises $A_1, A_2, \ldots A_n$:

If $\vDash B$, then $\vdash B$.

The proof of the completeness theorem is not at all simple, so I must defer to the appropriate literature.

Taken together, the soundness and completeness of calculus C demonstrate that C is an *adequate* calculus for statement logic. Using purely syntactic means, C identifies exactly the same formulas as logically true, and exactly the same inferences as valid, as does statement logic.

5. Review

Let us cast a glance back at the questions posed in section II.3. Perhaps most important was the question of the extent to which the logician is ever entitled to claim that a particular mode of inference has been justified. Conspiring against such claims is the fact that the criteria for the validity of an inference are built on the analysis of exemplary valid inferences. Furthermore, observer logic takes for granted the validity of an as yet unspecified set of inferences and inference modes. In qualitative terms, this situation amounts to a reflective equilibrium between exemplary valid inferences, object-logical criteria of validity, and observer-logical assumptions.

This situation is unsatisfactory because we always want to be as clear as possible in accounting for the presuppositions on which any theory is built. This is precisely where proof theory makes its contribution. It is absolutely clear which formulas it assumes to be logically true (the axioms of calculus C, Definition 4.8), and which inference rules may be used to generate further logical truths (modus ponens, or Rule D). What is also indisputable is the fact that these elements of the calculus are given absolutely no justification within the calculus itself; they are rather the touchstone for the justification of all of the formulas generated out of them. The contribution of observer logic is limited to the mechanical application of the deduction rule, and the insertion of formulas of the sort permitted by Definition 4.7, in place of the metavariables of the axiom schemata. All remaining issues of justification are left clearly focused on the axioms of C and the deduction rule.

6. Prospects for Predicate Logic

This final section, in which we take a peek at predicate logic, will be even more sketchy than the last. In predicate logic, we must labor under the burden of knowing that the decision problem has no general solution (section II.2.2.c). But here, as it happens, proof theory offers significant relief. For it is possible to construct an adequate calculus (known as "predicate calculus") for predicate logic. As we recall (compare section IV.4), the adequacy of a calculus consists in its being both sound and complete for the branch of logic in question, so that provability and derivability within the calculus coincide with the corresponding notions of logical truth and valid inference. In plain English, this means that there are calculi whose output precisely matches the set of PL-true formulas.

This result may give us a moment's pause. Did not the undecidability of predicate logic mean that there was in principle no possible mechanical decision procedure for determining the PL-truth of a PL formula? And would not an adequate calculus for predicate logic be just such a procedure, since the rules of this calculus, by definition, allow for the mechanical generation of all PL-true formulas? Is this not a contradiction? But the apparent contradiction vanishes on closer inspection of the adequacy result. The adequacy of a calculus means that there is a proof within this calculus for every PL-true formula. And this, in turn, means that every PL-true formula can be generated from the axioms by a finite series of applications of the deduction rules. And so while the actual *existence* of such a proof answers the question of a given formula's logical truth, this is of little help in those cases in which the status of a formula is genuinely unknown. The adequacy of a calculus only tells us that *if* a formula is PL-true, *then* it is provable within the calculus. But knowing that *if* the formula is PL-true, *then* it is provable does not help us to decide *whether* it is PL-true. If I have failed, after three days, or three months, or three years of trying, to come up with a proof of the PL-truth of a given formula, my failure might be due either to the fact that the formula is not PL-true or simply to the fact that I have failed to find the proof, although there is one. But deciding, in general, which of these possibilities holds just *is* the decision problem, and this problem is not solved by the existence of an adequate calculus.

To our knowledge of the adequacy of the aforementioned predicate calculus, we may also add a host of mechanical procedures for generating proofs within this calculus. In principle, some such procedures will eventually generate *all* such proofs. Their existence represents the best possible outcome, given undecidability. For any formula, these procedures will succeed, after a finite number of mechanical steps, in generating a proof—provided the proof exists! But—and this is the crux of undecidability—it is impossible to know in advance, for a given formula, whether the procedure will eventually come up with a proof or not, and so until it does the provability of the formula remains an open question.

I would like to close this overview by alluding to the logical results that rocked the worlds of logic and mathematics in the 1930s. These are the famous incompleteness theorems of Austrian mathematician and logician Kurt Gödel (1906–78). In order to comprehend them, one must first understand the concept of the formalization of a theory. The formalization of a theory begins with its axiomatization, the expression of a theory by means of a relatively small number of axioms, from which the remaining statements of the theory follow as logical consequences (compare section IV.1). Next, we abstract from the meanings of all descriptive terms in the theory, leaving only a logical form of the axioms. These formulas may then be taken as the premises of a logical calculus. What Gödel showed, by means of incontrovertible proof, is that a great many formalized theories are irreparably incomplete. This result applies, for example, to elementary arithmetic, the discipline to which such statements as $2 + 2 = 4$ or $2 \bullet 3 = 6$ belong. The incompleteness of arithmetic means: every conceivable formalization of arithmetic contains sentences that *can neither be proven nor refuted* within the formalization itself. In other words, every such formalization contains sentences A with the property that neither A nor $\neg A$ can be proven. Here formal logic comes face to face with its most fundamental limitations.

Appendix 1 ✳ An Additional Proof

The following is a proof of the theorem whose consequences for statement logic were discussed in section II.3.2. The theorem asserts that no SL formula can be logically true (or logically false) unless at least one of the sentential letters in it occurs more than once. This theorem holds only if we rule out connectives whose truth tables contain all Ts or all Fs in their main columns. We might call these "constant connectives." The truth tables for constant connectives $☺_1, ☹_1, ☺_2,$ and $☹_2$ are as follows:

A	$☺_1 A$	A	$☹_1 A$
T	T	T	F
F	T	F	F

A_1	A_2	$A_1 ☺_2 A_2$	A_1	A_2	$A_1 ☹_2 A_2$
T	T	T	T	T	F
T	F	T	T	F	F
F	T	T	F	T	F
F	F	T	F	F	F

The proof of the theorem proceeds by mathematical induction on the number of sentential letter tokens in a formula. The unhappy expression "sentential letter token" is designed to distinguish the total number of sentential letters in a given formula, irrespective of their sameness or difference, from the number of *different* sentential letters in the formula. The formula $p \wedge (q \rightarrow p)$, for example, contains three sentential letter tokens but only two different sentential letters.

First, a brief reminder on the method of proof by induction. It begins with a proof of the theorem for some baseline case, in this case for all formulas containing two sentential letter tokens, or $n = 2$. Next, we assume that the theorem is true for all formulas with 2, 3, . . . all the way on up to n-1 sentential letter tokens, which is called the induction assumption. On the basis of the induction assumption, we prove that the theorem also holds for all formulas with n sentential letter tokens, for some n. With this second step completed, we have proved the theorem for all natural numbers n. Why? Well, we proved it for $n = 2$. Therefore, by the second step, it holds for $n = 3$. Applying the second step again, the theorem holds of $n = 4$, and so on for all natural numbers n.

Here, then, is the precise formulation of the theorem, followed by its proof.

Theorem

Let F_n be an SL-true or SL-false formula with n sentential letter tokens, containing no constant connectives. Then F_n contains at most n-1 different sentential letters.

Proof

1. Proof of the theorem for $n = 2$. F_2 must have one of the following four forms: $p*q$, $\neg p*q$, $p*\neg q$, or $\neg p*\neg q$, where $*$ is some nonconstant connective. If p is distinct from q, then by the nonconstancy of $*$, F_2 can neither be SL-true nor SL-false. But since, by assumption, F_n is SL-true or SL-false, the two sentential letters must be the same.

2. Induction Assumption: Assume the theorem is true for formulas with 2, 3, . . . n-1 sentential letter tokens. On the basis of this assumption, we must prove it is true for formulas with n sentential letter tokens.

Without loss of generality, we may assume that F_n is not a negation. The reason is this. If F_n is in fact a negation, consider F'_n, where $F_n = \neg\neg \ldots \neg F'_n$ and F'_n itself is *not* a negation (F_n may have more than one negation sign at its beginning!). If we are able to prove that F'_n is a SL-truth or SL-falsehood, F_n will be, too. So in the following we will consider either the original F_n if it is not a negation, or F'_n if F_n is a negation, but rename it as F_n.

So, because F_n is not a negation, it must have one of the following four forms: F_m*F_{n-m}, $\neg F_m*F_{n-m}$, $F_m*\neg F_{n-m}$ or $\neg F_m*\neg F_{n-m}$, where $*$ is some nonconstant connective. One of two cases must apply.

Case 1: F_m or F_{n-m} is a SL-truth or SL-falsehood. In that case, by the induction assumption, the formula in question must contain at least one sentential letter that occurs at least twice. But then F_n must also contain at least one sentential letter that occurs at least twice; F_n contains at most n-1 different sentential letters.

Case 2: Neither F_m nor F_{n-m} is either a SL-truth or SL-falsehood. Let us now assume that all of the sentential letters in F_m differ from the sentential letters in F_{n-m}. Under this assumption, the truth values of F_m and F_{n-m} vary independently of one another under different interpretations; that is, every possible combination of truth values for the two subformulas occurs in the truth table of F_n. But then because * is a nonconstant connective, F_n cannot be either SL-true or SL-false. Since it *is* either SL-true or SL-false, the above assumption must be false, that is that at least one of the sentential letters in F_m must be the same as at least one of the sentential letters in F_{n-m}. Therefore, F_n contains at most n-1 different sentential letters. QED.

Appendix 2 ✳ Solutions to Exercises

By Christopher von Bülow and Alex Levine

Exercise 1.1

A = terrestrial animals; B = mammals; C = marine animals:

> Some terrestrial animals are mammals.
> Some mammals are marine animals.
> ✳

Therefore,   Some terrestrial animals are marine animals.

Alternatively,

A = women; B = feminists; C = men

> Some women are feminists.
> Some feminists are men.
> ✳

Therefore,   Some women are men.

Exercise 1.2

A = life forms; B = trees; C = taller than 6'5"

> Some life forms are trees.
> Some trees are taller than 6'5"
> ✳

Therefore,   Some life forms are taller than 6'5"

Alternatively,

A = prime numbers; B = numbers between 1 and 10; C = even
>Some prime numbers are numbers between 1 and 10.
>Some numbers between 1 and 10 are even.

>*

Therefore,   Some prime numbers are even.

When an inference is logically valid, it possesses the first feature shared by all valid inferences: when its premises are true, so is its conclusion. Conversely, when an inference lacks this feature, it is invalid. But these two claims still do not provide us with a feature of *invalid* inferences, for they do not rule out the existence of sneaky invalid inferences whose premises and conclusion are both true. Example 1.5, as an invalid inference, is in no way obligated to deliver a false conclusion from true premises, or a true conclusion from false premises, under every possible substitution. There are thus two sorts of invalid inferences: those that wear their invalidity on their sleeves, because they generate false from true, and those for which only closer scrutiny reveals the truth of the conclusion to be mere coincidence, or at any rate, not logically forced.

Exercise 1.3

The premises in Example 1.4 correspond to the diagrams:

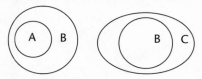

Together, they yield,

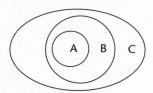

Which contains the conclusion,

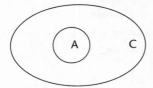

The premises of Example 1.5 may be represented in several different ways. Like this:

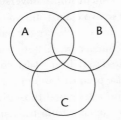

Or like this:

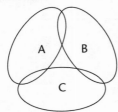

Or like this:

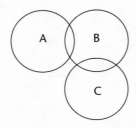

The first diagram implies the existence of *A*s that are both *B*s *and* *C*s; the second and third diagrams do not. In the first and second diagrams there are *A*s that are also *C*s (making the conclusion true), but not in the third. The premises are consistent with the first two diagrams, and thus with the truth of the conclusion, but they do not rule out the third diagram and thus fail to *guarantee* the truth of the conclusion. For this reason, the inference is invalid.

Exercise 1.4

First, a boring solution:

>   Some A are B.
>   Some B are C.
>   *
> Therefore, Some A are B.

And a more interesting solution:

>   Some A are B.
>   All B are C.
>   *
> Therefore, Some A are C.

Exercise 1.5

(1), (5), (7), and (10) are not statements. (1) is an exclamation, and (5) is an instruction. Though it might be mistaken for a statement, (7) is really a thinly veiled effort at intimidation. (10) is a question, one which may not have any definitive answer.

(2) may be classified as a statement, unless we read the sentence as expressing a speech act that becomes true by its very utterance.

(3) is perhaps most likely to be found in a fictional context, in which it could not be taken to refer to real objects. But within this context, the sentence is capable of being not only true but also necessarily true—unless, of course, we take it as an empty, formulaic closing, stylistically significant, perhaps, but no more a statement than an "amen" uttered in church. It is also possible to place (3) in a nonfic-

tional context, one in which it no longer expresses a necessary truth: it might refer to as yet unborn children.

(4) belongs to the class of conventional auxiliary expressions familiar from mathematical proofs, and it stipulates that n be taken as a placeholder for a natural number. Once this stipulation has taken place, (4) may be read as implying the statement (4´), "n is a natural number." But (4) and (4´) are not the same, for (4) fails to *assert* anything about a given object (say, the letter n or some natural number); it rather *makes something the case.*

Leaving aside the fact that (6) remains a grammatical fragment, it may nonetheless be read, in appropriate context, as expressing a statement. If, on returning to her car, person X discovers a notice stuck to her windshield on which (6) is written, she is likely to understand the sentence simply as an order to pay, an imperative. Under those circumstances, it would make little sense for her to approach the parking official with the objection, "No, this is false!" On the other hand, if this same notice is later shown to the shopkeeper in front of whose premises X has parked, or if (6) is read in a law text, it might very well be construed as a statement: "X is obliged to pay a \$200 fine for unauthorized parking" or "The fine for unauthorized parking is \$200."

(8) is most plausibly understood as a metaphorical expression of frustration and anger, and on this reading, it is no statement. But of course we may imagine someone so abused by fate as to venture a literal utterance of (8), understood as a realistic prognosis regarding his or her own mental health. Provided we have no scruples about determinism (and about a problem to be discussed below, in section II.1.1.d), as uttered in this context, (8) is a statement.

(9) is a version of what is known as the Liar Paradox. On the surface, it appears to be an ordinary declarative sentence and thus a prime candidate for statementhood. But if the sentence were true, then by its own assertion it would have to be false; if it were false, by the same reasoning, it would have to be true. Either assumption leads to contradiction. Despite its rather mundane grammatical form, we must exclude this sentence from the class of statements.

Exercise 1.6

(6) is most definitely no statement, for in addition to the statement "That's not right," it contains a question, "Or maybe it is?" The sentence, "After the lecture, Paul Hoyningen asked himself, 'Maybe that was right after all?'" is a different

case, for while it contains the same question, it does so only in direct quotation.

In order to understand the threat made in (1) or the wish expressed in (2) as statements, one would have to make quite a stretch, reading (1) as asserting something on the order of, "If you return, great harm will be done to you," and (2) as expressing (2′): "I hope that you will be doing well the next time I see you." But (2) has as little to do with (2′) as "Ow!" with "I am experiencing pain."

(3), (4), and (5) are clear instances of statements. But each raises certain initial doubts. In the case of (3), the 'I think' might throw us off, the appearance of 'true' is confusing in (4), and (5) has something to do with questions. Let us dispel these doubts.

(3) simply asserts, "I believe the following: If Fred goes out with Anne, then Sarah will be angry." The person uttering this sentence either believes the "if . . . then" sentence contained in it, or not (note that we must not confuse the absence of belief with disbelief; it is also possible to be uncertain).

(4) asserts the truth of a particular statement, or the factuality of a particular state of affairs, and as such it is either right (in which case [4] is true) or wrong ([4] is false).

Although the word 'asked' occurs in (5), it is hardly a question. Leaving aside the vagueness of the word 'recently', we are dealing with a straightforward instance of a statement about a particular speech act.

Exercise 1.7

1. Strictly speaking, the connective 'or' is not truth-functional. The reason for this somewhat startling claim is that the English word 'or' is ambiguous, expressing both inclusive and exclusive 'or.' To be sure, we can usually tell from context which is meant, but it is precisely this fact that makes 'or' an *intensional* connective. For the truth value of a statement containing this connective is not determined exclusively by the truth values of its constituent statements, but also by their meaning, which may or may not force either inclusive or exclusive reading of the 'or'. For their part, both inclusive and exclusive 'ors' are truth-functional (see section II.1.1.b).

2. 'Due to the fact that' is clearly not a truth-functional connective. To see this, consider the example "Fred passed the exam due to the fact that he had bribed the teaching assistant with a bottle of milk." Let us suppose that both of the constituent clauses are true. Neither the truth nor the falsehood of the state-

ment as a whole is thereby determined: it is possible that the bribe was the decisive factor in Fred's success, but it might equally well be the case that, contrary to expectations, the exams were graded by the professor, not the teaching assistant, and Fred passed because he knew the material anyway. So 'due to the fact that' is an intensional connective.

3. In general, 'If ... then ...' is an intensional connective. See section II.1.1.d, for further discussion.

Exercise 2.1

The truth table for the exclusive or, here represented by "XOR," is as follows:

A_1	A_2	A_1 XOR A_2
T	T	F
T	F	T
F	T	T
F	F	F

Exercise 2.2

    1. $S \wedge H$
    2. $S \wedge \neg H$
    3. $H \wedge \neg S$
    4. $\neg S \wedge \neg H$
    5. $\neg S$

Exercise 2.3

The statements and substatements being negated are as follows:

    1. A_2
    2. A_1
    3. $A_1 \wedge A_2$
    4. A_1 and $A_2 \wedge A_3$
    5. $A_1 \vee (A_2 \vee \neg A_3)$ and A_3
    6. $A \wedge \neg (\neg A_2 \vee A_3)$, $\neg A_2 \vee A_3$, and A_2

Exercise 2.4

1. $B \land F$
2. $B \land \neg F$
3. $\neg F \land \neg B$
4. $F \land B$
5. $\neg B \land F$
6. $\neg(B \land \neg F)$
7. $\neg(B \land F)$
8. $\neg(B \land F)$

Exercise 2.5

"A_1 XOR A_2" may be rewritten in any of the following ways:

$$(A_1 \lor A_2) \land \neg(A_1 \land A_2)$$
$$(A_1 \lor A_2) \land (\neg A_1 \lor \neg A_2)$$
$$(A_1 \land \neg A_2) \lor (A_2 \land \neg A_1)$$

Exercise 2.6

In these statements it is not always easy to see whether the correct abbreviation is "$A{\to}E$" or "$E{\to}A$"—even leaving other possibilities aside. Our first inclination, for example, might be to write (2) as "$E{\to}A$." In order to determine the correct order, we must be careful to ask, for each sentence, which of the two constituent statements E and A forces the truth of the other.

Let us return to (2): "Adam is coming only if Eve is also coming." It entails that if Eve is *not* coming, Adam is not, either. Or, in other words, if Adam *is* coming, then so is Eve: $A{\to}E$. In statement (2), Eve's presence in no way guarantee's Adam's, so we cannot say that $E{\to}A$. It might be that Adam is playing hard to get, and on hearing that Eve is coming, insists, "Well, great, then I'll *consider* coming, provided I also get a big tub of chocolate mousse." On pragmatic grounds we have reason to suppose that anyone uttering (2) wishes to express that Eve's presence is not only a necessary condition for Adam's ($A{\to}E$) but also sufficient ($E{\to}A$). On purely logical grounds, however, this supposition is unwarranted.

The 'only if' can easily mislead us, given our inclination to treat statements containing the conjunction 'if' (e.g., "If A_1, then A_2," or "A_2 only if A_1") as expressing causal relations, such as "A_1 *brings about* A_2." (2) makes it sound as though E were the cause of A; in any case, it certainly *does not* claim that A is the cause of E. Nonetheless, "$A{\to}E$" is the correct abbreviation; the tendency to associate the '$\to$' with causal connections is erroneous.

This tendency may be avoided by taking care to recall the definition of the conditional, $A_1{\to}A_2$, as $\neg(A_1{\wedge}\neg A_2)$. In the present case, this means we must understand statement (2) as ruling out that A is true and E simultaneously false, $(A{\wedge}\neg E)$. Consequently, "$A{\to}E$" must be the right abbreviation. On the other hand, if we wanted to rule out the possibility that E is true and A simultaneously false, $(E{\wedge}\neg A)$, we would say "$E{\to}A$." By now it should be clear that statement (2) is making the former assertion: it rules out the possibility of Adam's coming and Eve's simultaneously staying away, for Adam is coming, only if Eve is coming.

1. $A{\to}E$
2. $A{\to}E$ (or $\neg(A{\wedge}\neg E)$, or *conceivably* $(A{\to}E){\wedge}(E{\to}A)$ or $(A{\wedge}E){\vee}((\neg A){\wedge}\neg E))$
3. $E{\to}A$
4. $\neg(A{\wedge}\neg E)$ (or $A{\to}E$)
5. $(A{\to}E){\wedge}(E{\to}A)$ or $(A{\wedge}E){\vee}((\neg A){\wedge}\neg E)$
6. $E{\to}A$ (see discussion of [2])
7. $A{\to}E$
8. $\neg(E{\wedge}\neg A)$ (or $E{\to}A$)
9. $(E{\to}A){\wedge}(A{\to}E)$

Exercise 2.7.

Please note that these questions do *not* read "How many ways do you *know* . . .". A plausible answer to the first question is "16." We arrive at this number by considering how many different possible truth tables there are for a binary extensional connective *, where all such truth tables take the following form:

A_1	A_2	$A_1{*}A_2$
T	T	a
T	F	b
F	T	c
F	F	d

Thus expressed, our question reduces to how many possible ways there are of evaluating *a, b, c,* and *d* as the "outputs" of the "truth function," which takes the combination of truth values for A_1 and A_2 on a given line as its "argument." Since, for each of the four, the choice between T and F remains independent of the choices made for the other three, we have $2^4 = 16$ possibilities. However, if we take into account the difference between '$A_1 \wedge A_2$' and '$A_1 \wedge$ it is true that A_2' (see section II.1.1.f, for a discussion of this difference), then there are infinitely many different extensional connectives.

The second question is much more difficult to answer. There is a different intensional connective for every possible relation that might obtain between the contents of two statements. For example, we might stipulate that $A \infty B$ is true just in case B makes reference to more giraffes than A. In this case, the statement "Logic is a bore ∞ I like walnut ice cream" would be false, since both constituent statements make reference to precisely the same number of giraffes, namely none. By contrast, "Formal logic is an aesthetic joy ∞ the giraffes in the Philadelphia Zoo love walnut ice cream" would be true. It should be quite clear that there is an infinite number of such relations. We might even define a connective '$\times$' for every (natural or real) number x: $A \times B$ is true, just in case A and B each refers to exactly one number, a and b respectively, and a is at least x less than b.

Exercise 2.8.

1. $(B \vee F) \rightarrow I$, where B = "A burglary has occurred"; F = "A fire has occurred"; and I = "The insurance company pays for the damages."

2. $(B \rightarrow (E \wedge \neg T)) \wedge (\neg B \rightarrow (((D \wedge W) \vee C)) \wedge \neg ((D \wedge W) \wedge C))$, where B = "Bill goes to the movie"; E = "Ed goes to the movie"; T = "There's something good on TV"; D = "Bill does the dishes"; W = "Bill waters the plants"; C = "Bill calls his sweetheart."

3. $(((\neg F) \rightarrow S) \wedge \neg (F \vee \neg A)) \wedge (A \rightarrow S)$, or $(((\neg F) \rightarrow S) v (F \rightarrow A)) \wedge (A \rightarrow S)$, where F = "Frances comes"; S = "Sarah will be upset"; and A = "Alex comes."

4. $(S \wedge A) \rightarrow ((\neg C) \wedge \neg (B \vee D))$, where S = "Mr. Miller is sick"; A = "Ms. Meyers is absent"; C = "The contract will be signed"; B = "The board will meet"; D = "The board will set the dividend."

5. $\neg (I \rightarrow (Tv(R \vee F)))$, where I = "The roads ice up"; T = "The temperature is below freezing"; R = "It is raining"; F = "It is foggy."

Exercise 2.9.

In order to really capture *all* of the SFs, we must proceed systematically. First, the simplest of all SFs: *p*. Next, we take the main connective into account: $q{\rightarrow}r$. Now we progressively unpack the consequent: $q{\rightarrow}\neg v$; $q{\rightarrow}\neg(w{\wedge}x)$, $q{\rightarrow}\neg((\neg y){\wedge}x)$. Returning to $q{\rightarrow}r$, we unpack the antecedent: $(s{\leftrightarrow}t){\rightarrow}r$; $((\neg u){\leftrightarrow}t){\rightarrow}r$. All that remains to be considered are combinations of antecedent and consequent at different levels of resolution: $(s{\leftrightarrow}t){\rightarrow}\neg v$; $(s{\leftrightarrow}t){\rightarrow}\neg(w{\wedge}x)$, $(s{\leftrightarrow}t){\rightarrow}\neg((\neg t){\wedge}x)$. Note that in this last formula we must ensure that the second letter in the antecedent is identical with the first letter in the consequent, in accordance with the repeated occurrence of constituent statement *B*. To complete our list by further resolving the antecedent, $((\neg u){\leftrightarrow}t){\rightarrow}\neg v$; $((\neg u){\leftrightarrow}t){\rightarrow}\neg(w{\wedge}x)$, $((\neg u){\leftrightarrow}t){\rightarrow}\neg((\neg t){\wedge}x)$. There we have it: exactly thirteen SFs. Who would have thought?

Exercise 2.10.

1. Disjunction
2. Biconditional
3. Conditional
4. Disjunction
5. Conditional
6. Negation
7. Disjunction

Exercise 2.11

Only the following parentheses are needed:

1. $p{\wedge}q{\rightarrow}(q{\rightarrow}r)$
2. $p{\wedge}q{\rightarrow}q{\vee}r$
3. $p{\wedge}q{\leftrightarrow}q{\rightarrow}r$
4. $(p{\wedge}q){\wedge}(q{\rightarrow}r)$
5. $\neg(p{\vee}q){\rightarrow}p{\wedge}q$

Exercise 2.12.

1.

p	$\leftrightarrow$	$\neg$	$\neg$	p
T	**T**	T	F	T
F	**T**	F	T	F

2.

p	$\leftrightarrow$	p	$\wedge$	p
T	**T**	T	T	T
F	**T**	F	F	F

3.

p	$\leftrightarrow$	p	$\vee$	p
T	**T**	T	T	T
F	**T**	F	F	F

4.

p	$\wedge$	q	$\leftrightarrow$	q	$\vee$	p
T	T	T	**T**	T	T	T
T	F	F	**F**	F	T	T
F	F	T	**F**	T	T	F
F	F	F	**T**	F	F	F

5.

p	$\vee$	q	$\leftrightarrow$	q	$\vee$	p
T	T	T	**T**	T	T	T
T	T	F	**T**	F	T	T
F	T	T	**T**	T	T	F
F	F	F	**T**	F	F	F

6.

(p	$\wedge$	q)	$\wedge$	r	$\leftrightarrow$	p	$\wedge$	(q	$\wedge$	r)
T	T	T	T	T	**T**	T	T	T	T	T
T	T	T	F	F	**T**	T	F	T	F	F
T	F	F	F	T	**T**	T	F	F	F	T
T	F	F	F	F	**T**	T	F	F	F	F
F	F	T	F	T	**T**	F	F	T	T	T
F	F	T	F	F	**T**	F	F	T	F	T
F	F	F	F	F	**T**	F	F	F	F	F

7.

(p	∨	q)		∨	r	↔	p	∨		(q	∨	r)
T	T	T		T	T	**T**	T	T		T	T	T
T	T	T		T	F	**T**	T	T		T	T	F
T	T	F		T	T	**T**	T	T		F	T	T
T	T	F		T	F	**T**	T	T		F	F	F
F	T	T		T	T	**T**	F	T		T	T	T
F	T	T		T	F	**T**	F	T		T	T	F
F	F	F		T	T	**T**	F	T		F	T	T
F	F	F		F	F	**T**	F	F		F	F	F

8.

(p	→	q)		→	r		↔	p	→		(q	→	r)
T	T	T		T	T		**T**	T	T		T	T	T
T	T	T		F	F		**T**	T	F		T	F	F
T	F	F		T	T		**T**	T	T		F	T	T
T	F	F		T	F		**T**	T	T		F	T	F
F	T	T		T	T		**T**	F	T		T	T	T
F	T	T		F	F		**F**	F	T		T	F	F
F	T	F		T	T		**T**	F	T		F	T	T
F	T	F		F	F		**F**	F	T		F	T	F

9.

(p	→	q)		∧		(q	→	p)
T	T	T		**T**		T	T	T
T	F	F		**F**		F	T	T
F	T	T		**F**		T	F	F
F	T	F		**T**		F	T	F

10.

p	∨	¬	p
T	**T**	F	T
F	**T**	T	F

11.

p	∧	¬	p
T	**F**	F	T
F	**F**	T	F

Exercise 2.13.

1.

p	→		p	∨	q
T	**T**		T	T	T
T	**T**		T	T	F
F	**T**		F	T	T
F	**T**		F	F	F

2.

p	∧	q	→	p
T	T	T	**T**	T
T	F	F	**T**	T
F	F	T	**T**	F
F	F	F	**T**	F

3.

p	∧	(q	∨	r)	↔	(p	∧	q)	∨	(p	∧	r)
T	T	T	T	T	**T**	T	T	T	T	T	T	T
T	T	T	T	F	**T**	T	T	T	T	T	F	F
T	T	F	T	T	**T**	T	F	F	T	T	T	T
T	F	F	F	F	**T**	T	F	F	F	T	F	F
F	F	T	T	T	**T**	F	F	T	F	F	F	T
F	F	T	T	F	**T**	F	F	T	F	F	F	F
F	F	F	T	T	**T**	F	F	F	F	F	F	T
F	F	F	F	F	**T**	F	F	F	F	F	F	F

4.

p	∨	(q	∧	r)	↔	(p	∨	q)	∧	(p	∨	r)
T	T	T	T	T	**T**	T	T	T	T	T	T	T
T	T	T	F	F	**T**	T	T	T	T	T	T	F
T	T	F	F	T	**T**	T	T	T	T	T	T	T
T	T	F	F	F	**T**	T	T	T	T	T	T	F
F	T	T	T	T	**T**	F	T	T	T	F	T	T
F	F	T	F	F	**T**	F	T	T	F	F	F	F
F	F	F	F	T	**T**	F	F	F	F	F	T	T
F	F	F	F	F	**T**	F	F	F	F	F	F	F

5.

¬	(p	∧	q)	↔	¬	p	∨	¬	q
F	T	T	T	**T**	F	T	F	F	T
T	T	F	F	**T**	F	T	T	T	F
T	F	F	T	**T**	T	F	T	F	T
T	F	F	F	**T**	T	F	T	T	F

6.

¬	(p	∨	q)	↔	¬	p	∧	¬	q
F	T	T	T	**T**	F	T	F	F	T
F	T	T	F	**T**	F	T	F	T	F
F	F	T	T	**T**	T	F	F	F	T
T	F	F	F	**T**	T	F	T	T	F

7.

p	→	q	↔	¬	q	→	¬	p
T	T	T	**T**	F	T	T	F	T
T	F	F	**T**	T	F	F	F	T
F	T	T	**T**	F	T	T	T	F
F	T	F	**T**	T	F	T	T	F

Exercise 2.14

1.

(p	→	q)	∧	p	→	q
T	T	T	T	T	**T**	T
T	F	F	F	T	**T**	F
F	T	T	F	F	**T**	T
F	T	F	F	F	**T**	F

2.

(p	→	q)	∧	¬	q	→	¬	p
T	T	T	F	F	T	**T**	F	T
T	F	F	F	T	F	**T**	F	T
F	T	T	F	F	T	**T**	T	F
F	T	F	T	T	F	**T**	T	F

3.

p	∧	¬	p	→	q
T	F	F	T	**T**	T
T	F	F	T	**T**	F
F	F	T	F	**T**	T
F	F	T	F	**T**	F

4.

p	→	q	∨	¬	q
T	**T**	T	T	F	T
T	**T**	F	T	T	F
F	**T**	T	T	F	T
F	**T**	F	T	T	F

5.

(p	∧	q)	∧	¬	q
T	T	T	**F**	F	T
T	F	F	**F**	T	F
F	F	T	**F**	F	T
F	F	F	**F**	T	F

Exercise 2.15

1.   If stupidity can be learned, then there are many diligent students.

   If there are many diligent students, then teachers are content.

   *

Therefore,   If stupidity can be learned, then teachers are content.

Expressed in terms of the most fine-grained SFs of the three statements, the inference is as follows:

$$p \to q$$
$$q \to r$$
*

Therefore, $p \to r$

By definition 2.11, we must show:

$$\vDash (p \to q) \wedge (q \to r) \to (p \to r)$$

which is accomplished by means of the appropriate truth table:

(p	→	q)	∧	(q	→	r)	→	(p	→	r)
T	T	T	T	T	T	T	**T**	T	T	T
T	T	T	F	T	F	F	**T**	T	F	F
T	F	F	F	F	T	T	**T**	T	T	T
T	F	F	F	F	T	F	**T**	T	F	F
F	T	T	T	T	T	T	**T**	F	T	T
F	T	T	F	T	F	F	**T**	F	T	F
F	T	F	T	F	T	T	**T**	F	T	T
F	T	F	T	F	T	F	**T**	F	T	F

2. By its nature, the body is divisible.

> If body and soul are one and the same, then the soul is
> divisible.
> But by its nature, the soul is indivisible.
> *

Therefore,   body and soul are not one and the same.

Let us begin by rewriting this inference by means of connectives and appropriate
abbreviations:

> *BD*
>
> *BSS→SD*
>
> *¬SD*
>
> *

Therefore,   *¬BSS*

The abbreviations are *BD* = "The body is divisible by nature"; *SD* = "The soul
is divisible (by nature)"; and *BSS* = "The body and soul are one and the same."
The inference thus has the form,

> *p*
>
> *q→r*
>
> *¬r*
>
> *

Therefore,   *¬q*

To determine its validity, we must test whether $\models (p \wedge (q \rightarrow r)) \wedge \neg r \rightarrow \neg q$.

(As an aside, we might ask why we have bothered to enclose the first two
premises in our premise conjunction within their own pair of parentheses. In natural language, when asserting conjunctions [or disjunctions] with more than two
constituents, we seldom trouble ourselves to make clear which of these constituents hang together more closely than the others. But when we have made up
our minds to pay such close attention to the forms of statements, then we really
must determine whether in a given statement [or formula] with the form *a*b*c*
(where * is any binary connective) the first * connects *a* with *b,* or *a* with *b*c;*
whether what is meant is actually (*a*b*)*c,* or a*(*b*c*). This question acquires

practical significance, for example, in our completion of the following truth table, in which without the outermost pair of parentheses, we would have no clear way of deciding which of the two '∧' to evaluate first. For clearly, there is no way of assessing them simultaneously! In II.2.5.c.4, however, we will come to see that with regard to the connectives ∧ and ∨, it makes no logical difference where we set our parentheses, so that in the end we may omit these parentheses after all. In the construction of truth tables, we may then evaluate such conjunctions and disjunctions in whichever order we prefer.)

As revealed by the following truth table, inferences of the form in question really are valid:

(p	∧	(q	→	r))	∧	¬	r	→	¬	q
T	T	T	T	T	F	F	T	**T**	F	T
T	F	T	F	F	F	T	F	**T**	F	T
T	T	F	T	T	F	F	T	**T**	T	F
T	T	F	T	F	T	T	F	**T**	T	F
F	F	T	T	T	F	F	T	**T**	F	T
F	F	T	F	F	F	T	F	**T**	F	T
F	F	F	T	T	F	F	T	**T**	T	F
F	F	F	T	F	F	T	F	**T**	T	F

3. Using the abbreviations S = "Subjectivism is correct." U = "Utilitarianism is correct," and R = "Ethical concepts are reducible to empirical concepts," we may represent the inference as follows:

$$S \lor U \to R$$
$$\neg S \land \neg U$$
$$*$$

Therefore, $\neg R$

An analysis of the most fine-grained corresponding SL formula, $(p \lor q \to r) \land (\neg p \land \neg q) \to \neg r$, yields the following truth table:

(p	∨	q	→	r)	∧	(¬	p	∧	¬	q)	→	¬	r
T	T	T	T	T	F	F	T	F	F	T	**T**	F	T
T	T	T	F	F	F	F	T	F	F	T	**T**	T	F
T	T	F	T	T	F	F	T	F	T	F	**T**	F	T
T	T	F	F	F	F	F	T	F	T	F	**T**	T	F
F	T	T	T	T	F	T	F	F	F	T	**T**	F	T
F	T	T	F	F	F	T	F	F	F	T	**T**	T	F
F	F	F	T	T	T	T	F	T	T	F	**F**	F	T
F	F	F	T	F	T	T	F	T	T	F	**T**	T	F

Because the main column does *not* contain only *T*s, it is *not* the case that

$$\vDash (p \lor q \to r) \land (\neg p \land \neg q) \to \neg r$$

Because the other SFs of this inference are all "coarser," it is plainly invalid. As an aside, it is worth noting that this inference is a somewhat more complicated example of the famous fallacy of denying the antecedent, concluding $\neg q$ from $p \to q$ and $\neg p$.

4. At first blush, the inferential chain leading from "He who reads the *NZZ*" to "is never hung-over" might seem valid. If we bend the example a bit, reading "He who reads the *NZZ*" as the statement, "*X* reads the *NZZ*," the following inference would appear to be up for formal investigation:

$$p$$
$$p \to q$$
$$q \to r$$
$$r \to s$$
$$s \to t$$
$$t \to u$$
$$u \to v$$
$$*$$

Therefore, v

Anyone who wishes is welcome to probe the corresponding conditional for logical truth (though you must not forget a single one of the many parentheses—recall our discussion of Exercise 2!). In fact, the proposed SF for the inference *is* valid. And because all of the premises strike us as more or less plausible, we are tempted, momentarily, to conclude that reading the *NZZ* serves as a marvelous preventative for hangovers. The trouble is that, despite appearances, the proposed SF is not really an SF for the inference in question. The illusion is fostered by a series of equivocations; for example, "takes the high ground" does not mean the same thing on the fourth line as it does on the fifth. The former occurrence is metaphorical, the latter literal. Furthermore, "falls off the wagon" is meant literally in the third-to-last line but figuratively (as a metaphor for going on a bender) in the second-to-last line.

Exercise 2.16

While (b) is a logical consequence of (a), (a) does not follow from (b). Let us first abbreviate the constituent atomic statements of (a) and (b): D = "The company is required to pay compensatory damages"; C = "The company is a corporation"; and F = "The company was founded no later than 1989." This yields,

   a. $D \leftrightarrow C \wedge F$
   b. $(C \rightarrow F \wedge D) \wedge (\neg C \rightarrow \neg F \wedge \neg D)$

The aforementioned relations of logical consequence may now be articulated in terms of the corresponding fine-grained SFs:

   1. $(q \rightarrow r \wedge p) \wedge (\neg q \rightarrow \neg r \wedge \neg p)$ does not follow from $p \leftrightarrow q \wedge r$.
   2. $p \leftrightarrow q \wedge r$ follows from $(q \rightarrow r \wedge p) \wedge (\neg q \rightarrow \neg r \wedge \neg p)$.

By Definitions 2.11.1 and 2.9.1, (1) amounts to the claim that

$$(p \leftrightarrow q \wedge r) \rightarrow (q \rightarrow r \wedge p) \wedge (\neg q \rightarrow \neg r \wedge \neg p)$$

is not true under all extensional interpretations. Assigning truth values F, T, and F to sentential letters p, q, and r, respectively, we obtain,

$(p$	$\leftrightarrow$	q	$\wedge$	$r)$	$\rightarrow$	$(q$	$\rightarrow$	r	$\wedge$	$p)$	$\wedge$	$(\neg$	q	$\rightarrow$	$\neg$	r	$\wedge$	$\neg$	$p)$
F	T	T	F	F	**F**	T	F	F	F	F	F	F	T	T	T	F	T	T	F

thus establishing the existence of an extensional interpretation on which the conditional is false, proving (1). (This proof would be longer if we were required to show how we had arrived at this interpretation in the first place. Constructing the entire truth table is doubtless the method requiring the least thought.)

To establish (2), we must examine the appropriate truth table:

(q	→	r	∧	p)	∧	(¬	q	→	¬	r	∧	¬	p)	→	(p	↔	q	∧	r)
T	T	T	T	T	T	F	T	T	F	T	F	F	T	**T**	T	T	T	T	T
T	F	F	F	T	F	F	T	T	T	F	F	F	T	**T**	T	F	T	F	F
F	T	T	T	T	F	T	F	F	F	T	F	F	T	**T**	T	F	F	F	T
F	T	F	F	T	F	T	F	F	T	F	F	F	T	**T**	T	F	F	F	F
T	F	T	F	F	F	F	T	T	F	T	F	T	F	**T**	F	F	T	T	T
T	F	F	F	F	F	F	T	T	T	F	T	T	F	**T**	F	T	T	F	F
F	T	T	F	F	F	T	F	F	F	T	F	T	F	**T**	F	F	F	F	T
F	T	F	F	F	T	T	F	F	T	F	T	T	F	**T**	F	T	F	F	F

Exercise 2.17

Evaluating a formula "economically" means doing only the minimum work necessary. It does *not* mean calculating truth values in one's head. If our task, for example, is to evaluate a formula $p \wedge A$, where A is itself a complex formula, we need not bother to evaluate A in those cases in which p is already assigned value F; we already know the conjunction is false. Similar labor-saving devices are available for → and ∨, though not for ¬ and ↔. But there is no excuse for failing to write down all the truth values assigned to the *sentential letters*, even when they are not all needed at a given stage of evaluation. The combination of truth values assigned to the sentential letters is, after all, what distinguishes the extensional interpretations represented on successive lines of a truth table.

If we wish to be *systematic* in our evaluation of a formula while remaining economical, we must treat every line of the truth table as follows: Unless the formula is a negation, in which case there are no shortcuts, we begin by comparing the two subformulas on either side of the main connective. Next we perform an economical evaluation of the shorter of the two (or the nicer one, if both are the same length). If this result determines the truth value for the entire formula, we write the value down in the appropriate column and proceed to the next line. Otherwise, we must first evaluate the second subformula.

	p	→	(q	→	p)
1.	T	**T**	T	T	T
	T	**T**	F	T	T
	F	**T**	T		F
	F	**T**	F		F

2.

p	→	(q	→	p	∧	q)
T	**T**	T	T	T	T	T
T	**T**	F	T	T		F
F	**T**	T		F		T
F	**T**	F		F		F

3.

p	→	(¬	p	→	q)
T		**T**	T	T	T
T	**T**	F	T	T	F
F	**T**		F		T
F	**T**		F		F

4.

p	→	((p	→	q)	→	q)
T	**T**	T	T	T	**T**	T
T	**T**	T	F	F	**T**	F
F	**T**	F	T			T
F	**T**	F	F			F

5.

q	→	(p	→	p)
T	**T**	T	T	T
T	**T**	F	T	F
F	**T**	T		T
F	**T**	F		F

We do not have an exact definition of what Ackermann meant by "strict implication." What we do know is that strict implication is meant to hold just in case there is genuine truth transfer from antecedent to consequent, meaning that the truth of the consequent really *depends* on the truth of the antecedent. Unlike the material conditional, a strict implication cannot be made true simply by the necessary (e.g., logical) falsehood of the antecedent (in which case the consequent is never "implicated" at all) or the necessary (e.g., logical) truth of the consequence. (However, *some* formulas of this sort are logically true even in Ackermann's strict sense. For example, $p \wedge \neg p \rightarrow p \wedge \neg p$ and $p \vee \neg p \rightarrow p \vee \neg p$ remain logically true, because they are instances of the formula $p \rightarrow p$, which is tautological even if we insist on strict implication.)

Why, then, on the strict reading of '$\rightarrow$' must we reject the logical truth of formulas 1–5? Let us consider (1), $p \rightarrow (q \rightarrow p)$. If this formula were logically true, it would have to be true under all intensional interpretations—the statement

$A{\rightarrow}(B{\rightarrow}A)$ would be true for every assignment of statements to A and B. But that would mean that $B{\rightarrow}A$ would have to be true for any true statement A and any statement B, in which case any statement B strictly implies every true statement A, regardless of whether A and B have anything to do with one another. Clearly this is not the case. By modus tollens, we conclude that formula (1), read in Ackermann's sense, is not logically true.

Analogous arguments apply to formulas (2), (3), and (4). Formula (5) deviates from this pattern in that its consequent remains a logical truth even in Ackermann's sense. Still, this same sense requires that we reject the logical truth of (5), because it would entail that any statement B implies all logically true statements of the form $A{\rightarrow}A$, even though, in general, A and B have nothing to do with one another, and the truth of $A{\rightarrow}A$ fails to depend on that of B.

Exercise 2.18

As customary, we will prove the stated equivalences by constructing the appropriate truth tables. In the interests of saving parentheses, we will assume that the Sheffer Stroke takes precedence in the order of operations over the biconditional, allowing us to write formulas of the form $F{\leftrightarrow}(G|H)$ as $F{\leftrightarrow}G|H$ (for formulas F, G, and H).

1.

¬	p	↔	p	|	p
F	T	**T**	T	F	T
T	F	**T**	F	T	F

2.

p	∧	q	↔	(p	|	q)	|	(p	|	q)
T	T	T	**T**	T	F	T	T	T	F	T
T	F	F	**T**	T	T	F	F	T	T	F
F	F	T	**T**	F	T	T	F	F	T	T
F	F	F	**T**	F	T	F	F	F	T	F

For the next three, we return to our labor-saving "economical" procedure, exploiting the fact that once either side of the exclusion is false, the exclusion itself is known to be true.

3.

p	∨	q	↔	(p	|	p)	|	(q	|	q)
T	T	T	**T**	T	F	T	T	T		T
T	T	F	**T**	T	F	T	T	F		F
F	T	T	**T**	F		F	T	T	F	T
F	F	F	**T**	F	T	F	F	F	T	F

4.

p	→	q	↔	p	|	(q	|	q)
T	T	T	**T**	T	T	T	F	T
T	F	F	**T**	T	F	F	T	F
F	T	T	**T**	F	T	T		T
F	T	F	**T**	F	T	F		F

5.

(p	↔	q)	↔	(p	|	q)	|	((p	|	p)	|	(q	|	q)
T	T	T	T	**T**	T	F	T	T	T	T		T		T
T	F	F	F	**T**	T	T	F	F	T	F	T	T	F	F
F	F	T	T	**T**	F	T	T	F	F	F	T	T	F	T
F	T	F	F	**T**	F	T	F	T	F	T	F	F	F	T

In colloquial terms, we may gloss the Sheffer Stroke as expressing "not both," so that "$F|G$" reads, "not both F and G" (not to be confused with "neither," as in "neither F nor G"!).

The following equivalences may be demonstrated with equal ease:

$$p|q \equiv \neg(p \wedge q) \equiv \neg p \vee \neg q \equiv p \rightarrow \neg q$$

Exercise 2.19.

1. $\neg(\neg p \vee \neg q) \vee \neg(\neg p \vee \neg r)$

$\equiv (\neg\neg p \wedge \neg\neg q) \vee (\neg\neg p \wedge \neg\neg r)$ (De Morgan, twice)

$\equiv (p \wedge q) \vee (p \wedge r)$ (Double negation, four times)

$\equiv p \wedge (q \vee r)$ (Distributive law)

2. $\neg(\neg p \vee \neg(q \vee \neg(\neg p \vee q)))$

$\equiv \neg\neg p \wedge \neg\neg(q \vee (\neg\neg p \vee \neg q))$ (De Morgan, twice)

$\equiv p \wedge (q \vee (p \wedge \neg q))$ (Double negation, three times)

$\equiv (p \wedge q) \vee (p \wedge (p \wedge \neg q))$ (Distributive law)

$\equiv (p \wedge q) \vee ((p \wedge p) \wedge \neg q)$ (Associative law)

$\equiv (p \wedge q) \vee (p \wedge \neg q)$ (Principle of tautology)

$\equiv p \wedge (q \vee \neg q)$ (Distributive law)

$\equiv p$ (*)

(*) takes the place of a proof that $\vDash p \wedge (q \vee \neg q) \leftrightarrow p$. More generally, it is possible to show that $\vDash A$ entails $p \wedge A \equiv p$.

3. $p{\rightarrow}(q{\rightarrow}p{\wedge}q)$

$\equiv \neg(p{\wedge}\neg(q{\rightarrow}p{\wedge}q))$	(Definition of $\rightarrow$)
$\equiv \neg(p{\wedge}\neg\neg(q{\wedge}\neg(p{\wedge}q)))$	(Definition of $\rightarrow$)
$\equiv \neg(p{\wedge}(q{\wedge}\neg(p{\wedge}q)))$	(Double negation)
$\equiv \neg((p{\wedge}q){\wedge}\neg(p{\wedge}q))$	(Associative law)
$\equiv \neg(p{\wedge}q){\vee}\neg\neg(p{\wedge}q)$	(De Morgan)
$\equiv \neg(p{\wedge}q){\vee}(p{\wedge}q)$	(Double negation)
$\equiv (p{\wedge}q){\vee}\neg(p{\wedge}q)$	(Commutative law)
$\equiv T$	(*)

Let boldface 'T' serve as an abbreviation, $T = p{\vee}\neg p$. Alternatively, we might simply call it "The Tautology," because for any formula G, $G \equiv T$ just in case $\vDash G$. This definition gives us another way of expressing the logical truth of a formula. (Analogously, we might let $F = \neg T$, in which case, for any formula G, $G \equiv F$ just in case $\vDash \neg G$.) The final equivalence, (*), follows from $\vDash r{\vee}\neg r$ (Exercise 2.12.10) together with one application of the Substitution Theorem, yielding $\vDash (p{\wedge}q){\vee}\neg(p{\wedge}q)$.

Exercise 2.20

Let A and B be any two statement-logically contradictory statements. By Definition 2.14, it follows that $A{\leftrightarrow}B$ must be logically false; i.e., the truth values of A and B are always opposed. Therefore the conjunction $A{\wedge}B$ is a logical falsehood, because one or the other conjunct of $A{\wedge}B$ will always have truth value F. But this is precisely the criterion of logical contrariness established in Definition 2.13.

Exercise 2.21

1. The assertion that A is both necessary and sufficient for B means that both $B{\vDash}A$ and $A{\vDash}B$, or alternatively, that formulas $B{\rightarrow}A$ and $A{\rightarrow}B$ are both logically true. This, in turn, is equivalent to the logical truth of $(B{\rightarrow}A){\wedge}(A{\rightarrow}B)$. At the same time, the assertion that $A \equiv B$ means that $A{\leftrightarrow}B$ is logically true. So to prove the assigned claim, we must show that $(A{\rightarrow}B){\wedge}(B{\rightarrow}A)$ and $A{\leftrightarrow}B$ are logically equivalent. This is easily accomplished by verifying the logical truth of $(A{\rightarrow}B){\wedge}(B{\rightarrow}A){\leftrightarrow}(A{\leftrightarrow}B)$.

2. Let arbitrary formulas F and G be given. The claim is that if either (a) $F \equiv$

G, or (b), *F* and *G* are contrary, or (c), *F* and *G* are contradictory, then *F* and *G* are logically dependent.

a. Let $F \equiv G$. By Definition 2.12, this means that $\vDash F \leftrightarrow G$. In that case, *F* and *G* always have the same truth values, under every extensional interpretation. In particular, *G* must be true under every extensional interpretation that makes *F* true (this does not mean that there is necessarily *any* extensional interpretation on which *F* is true, only that *if* there is, that same interpretation also makes *G* true.). In that case, however, $F \rightarrow G$ is true on every extensional interpretation. Therefore, $\vDash F \rightarrow G$, hence $F \vDash G$. So *F* and *G* are logically dependent.

b. Let *F* and *G* be contraries. By Definition 2.13, this means that $F \wedge G$ is logically false. In other words, every extensional interpretation that makes *F* true must make *G* false, or $\neg G$ true. But in that case, $F \rightarrow \neg G$ is a logical truth—$\vDash F \rightarrow \neg G$—which entails that $F \vDash \neg G$. So again, *F* and *G* are logically dependent.

c. Let *F* and *G* be contradictory. By Definition 2.14, this means that $F \leftrightarrow G$ is logically false, or that under every extensional interpretation, *F* and *G* must always have opposite truth values. So every extensional interpretation that makes *F* true must make *G* false. But as demonstrated in part (b) above, this establishes the logical dependence of *F* and *G*.

Exercise 3.1

The following listing canvasses only some of the more obvious analyses and is not intended to be exhaustive.

Number of Subject:	Predicate:	Places:
1. Veronica	. . . is sitting at the table	1
(Veronica, the table)	. . . is sitting . . .	2
2. (Veronica, Stephen)	. . . and . . . are sitting at the table	2
(Veronica, Stephen, the table)	. . . and . . . are sitting at . . .	3
Veronica	. . . and Stephen are sitting at the table	1
3. Veronica	. . . is sitting across from Stephen	1
(Veronica, Stephen)	. . . is sitting across from . . .	2

4. Chicago	. . . is on Lake Michigan	1
(Chicago, Lake Michigan)	. . . is on . . .	2

5. "There are three bathers on the beach" is *not* a singular statement, for "three bathers" does not designate a *single* object, or an individual in our sense. Nor does it designate a *triple* of individuals, unlike (Veronica, Stephen, the table) on the second reading of exercise (2) above. Suppose the three bathers in question are Anne, Bert, and Chris. To be sure, (Anne, Bert, Chris) would be *an* appropriate logical subject for an individual statement, but so would (Bert, Chris, Anne). The claim that any one of the six possible triples is *the* logical subject, and not one of the others, is completely arbitrary, as the statement in question asserts nothing of the sort. This argument does not rule out the *unordered* set {Anne, Bert, Chris} as subject, but it might be objected, with reason, that *sets* are not generally the sorts of things that lie about on the beach. Further, if we read our statement as asserting not "There are *exactly* three bathers . . ." but rather "There are *at least* three bathers . . ." then the statement remains true if in addition to bathers Anne, Bert, and Chris, bather Doris is also on the beach. Once again, the statement offers us no help in deciding between the candidate subjects {Anne, Bert, Chris}, {Anne, Chris, Doris}, or possibly {Anne, Bert, Chris, Doris}. Matters would be different if we were talking about three *particular* bathers. In the statement, "The Three Musketeers are on the beach," we might easily read the logical subject as {Athos, Porthos, Aramis}. So we would have an easier time of it if sentence (5) read, "*The* three bathers are on the beach," where the three bathers were understood as particular people. Still, there remains one way of analyzing sentence (5) as a singular statement:

Subject:	Predicate:	Number of Places:
The beach	Three bathers are on . . .	1
6. Lecturer S	. . . ordinarily begins her lectures promptly	1
(Lecturer S, S's lecture)	. . . ordinarily begins . . . promptly	2

7. There are at least three ways of interpreting this seventh sentence. Understood in its proverbial sense, it reminds us that it is better to work to achieve manageable goals than to strive toward some unattainable utopia. Second, it can be read as a comment on the locality-dependent qualities of birds: "for all birds *x, y,*

and z, when x is in the hand and y and z are in the bush, and x, y, and z are distinct, then x is better than y and z" (leaving open, for the moment, the question of whose hand, which bush, and what sense of "better" we have in mind). Finally, we might take (7) as a concrete assertion about three particular birds (and possibly one particular hand and one particular bush): "Benny the sparrow in the hand is better than Alice the dove and Charlie the duck in the bush." Surely the proverbial interpretation best captures the likely meaning of any utterance of (7). Unfortunately, this reading remains somewhat resistant to formal logical analysis, referring as it does not to things, but to kinds of states of affairs or behavioral responses to them. As we shall see, the second, more literal interpretation is of greater interest to predicate logic, albeit not as an example of a singular statement. Finally, the third, or "hyperliteral" reading, though furthest from the conventional proverbial sense, is most susceptible to treatment given the resources currently at our disposal. We might render it as follows (using connectives as abbreviations):

Subject:	Predicate:	Number of Places:
(Benny, Alice, Charlie)	x in the hand $\wedge$ y in the bush $\wedge$ z in the bush $\rightarrow$ x is better than y $\wedge$ x is better than z	3

8. The analysis of this statement faces all of the problems cited in discussion of (5) and (7).

9. At first blush, this structure of this sentence appears to be extraordinarily simple:

Subject:	Predicate:	Number of Places:
It	. . . is raining	1

But we are in deep trouble once we ask what "it" is supposed to be. A raindrop? A particular collection of raindrops? A cloud? A region? Sentence (9) is best treated as a figure of speech, whose grammatical form provides poor guidance as to logical form. Two possible interpretations are:

Subject:	Predicate:	Number of Places:
region X	it is raining in . . .	1
The weather in region X	. . . is rainy	1

10. Here, too, we are tempted by an erroneous interpretation:

Subject:	Predicate:	Number of Places:
someone	. . . is sitting at the table	1

After all, isn't "someone" just a placeholder for some as yet to be determined particular person? Won't the context of this utterance make it clear which someone is meant, just as it reveals which table is meant? Let us perform the following complex thought experiment: Peeking into my dormitory kitchen, I see Angie sitting at the table. I pop into my room for a moment, and on my way out, I run into Gaby in the hall, on her way to the kitchen. In a gossipy mood, I whisper to her, "There is someone sitting at the table," thinking that Angie has remained seated. So in this context, the "someone" is Angie, leading to the following interpretation of sentence (10):

Subject:	Predicate:	Number of Places:
Angie	. . . is sitting at the table	1

But let us further suppose that while I was in my room, Angie has left the kitchen and Dirk has taken her place at the table. Gaby enters the kitchen, sees Dirk, and turning back to the hall, shouts, "You were right!" And Gaby is right, too, because someone *is* sitting at the table, and so my earlier utterance of sentence (10) is *true*. Nonetheless, the sentence "Angie is sitting at the table" is now false, though it was true when I looked into the kitchen. To be sure, the context appears to have changed while I was in my room, suggesting that the meaning of sentence (10) may have changed as well. But has it? No, because *even in a specific context* this sentence *does not* refer to a *particular* person. What it asserts is rather that *someone or another* is sitting at the table. Or consider another example: I am lying in my bed one morning, trying to sleep. But through the thin wall separating my room from the kitchen, I hear this constant clatter, which keeps me awake. This is enough to tell me that *someone* is sitting at the kitchen table scraping out the jam jar, but I do not know whether it is Hermione, or Ron, or perhaps both of them. In that case, whom could the "someone" of sentence (10) stand for? And if *both* Hermione and Ron are sitting at the kitchen table, eking the very last out of the jam jar, then is Hermione the "someone," or is it Ron? Or both of them? Or the pair? The set? Barring the following highly unsatisfactory interpretation, there seems to be no way of interpreting sentence (10) as a singular statement:

Subject:	Predicate	Number of Places:
the table	someone is sitting at . . .	1

11. This sentence has a great deal in common with the previous example (not surprisingly, since the two are evidently contradictory). But in this case it is somewhat easier to see that the *grammatical* subject could not possibly be the *logical* subject. For who is "nobody"? To be sure, we sometimes say of someone, metaphorically, that he or she is *a* nobody, but we still cannot point to the person and say, "That's nobody." For if there is someone there to point at, that person must be *somebody*. Or perhaps we should understand "nobody" as designating some other sort of object, though not a person. One such candidate is the empty set of people. But can sets sit? If so, they would seem to be able to sit and stand at the same time, for both sentence (11) and "Nobody is *standing* at the table" could both simultaneously be true. Indeed, a brief reflection shows this set to have truly superhuman capabilities—at least on the present hypothesis. Rejecting any such assumptions, there is still a way of reading sentence (11) as a singular statement about the empty set:

Subject:	Predicate:	Number of Places:
∅	. . . = the set of people sitting at the table	1

But this analysis applies to the whole sentence. Our earlier gloss of the predicate, ". . . is sitting at the table," simply cannot be applied to sets.

Exercise 3.2

1. $\wedge x$ (x is pretty)   Domain: bridges
2. $\wedge x$ (x is pretty)   Domain: long bridges
   $\wedge x$ (x is long → x is pretty)   Domain: bridges
3. $\wedge x$ (x loves Fred)   Domain: people
4. $\wedge x$ (Fred loves x)   Domain: people
5. $\wedge x$ (x loves Fred)   Domain: people
6. $\wedge x$ (x was unhappy at that time)   Domain: people
7. The following interpretation is   Domain: points on the circumference
   mistaken: $\wedge x$ (x is equidistant from
   the center of the circle)

With or without the quantifier, "x is equidistant from the center of the circle" makes no sense. Equidistant with *what*? Surely we do not mean to suggest that each point, *all by itself,* has the mysterious property of equidistance, but rather that all such points *coincide* in their distance from the center. And such coincidence is not a property of individual points, but a relationship among all the points on a circumference. Fortunately, it is possible to express this relationship without recourse to infinite-place predicates. We must simply assert of all *pairs* (2-tupels) of points that both of their members agree in their distance to the center. Toward this end, we apply the two-place predicate, ". . . is the same distance from the center of the circle as . . . ," obtaining,

$\wedge x \wedge y$ (x is the same distance from the center of the circle as y)
Domain: points on the circumference

Or alternatively,

$\wedge x \wedge y$ (x's distance from the center of the circle = y's distance from the center of the circle)   Domain: points on the circumference

Note that the latter reading makes use of the equals sign; see section III.1.1.d.2.

Exercise 3.3

1. $\vee x$ (x is pretty)   Domain: houses
2. $\vee x$ (x is pretty)   Domain: things
3. $\vee x$ (x is climbing the Matterhorn)   Domain: people

4. ∨x (Fred sees x)   Domain: people
5. ∨x (x sees Fred)   Domain: people
6. ∨x (Karl-Adam lies at x)   Domain: points in time
7. ¬∨x (x is in the house)   Domain: people
8. ¬∨x (x knows the thief)   Domain: people
9. ¬∨x¬(x has thorns)   Domain: roses
10. ∨x (x lies between   Domain: nice cities
   North Cape and Sicily)
11. ∨x (x is a dog) ∧ ∨x (x is a cat)   Domain: {dogs}∪{cats}

Exercise 3.4.

1. Everyone trusts x. (x is trustworthy.)
2. x is trusting. (x trusts everyone.)
3. Everyone distrusts y.
4. x is mistrustful. (x distrusts everyone.)
5. Someone trusts y.
6. x trusts someone.
7. x punches everyone.

Exercise 3.5.

1. ¬∨y (x loves y)   Domain: people
2. ∧y (y knows x)   Domain: people
3. ∧y (x loves y)   Domain: people
4. ∧y (y loves x)   Domain: people
   [or possibly, ∧y (y knows x)]
5. ¬∧y¬(y loves x)   Domain: people
   [or ∨y (y loves x)]
6. ∧y (y loves x)   Domain: people
   [or possibly, ∧y (y knows x)]
7. ¬∧y¬(y knows x)   Domain: people
   [or ∨y (y knows x)]
8. ∧y (x helps y)   Domain: people
9. ∧y (y helps x)   Domain: people
10. ∨y (x helps y)   Domain: people

Exercise 3.6

In order to express the claim that a given domain contains (at least) two (distinct) objects with a particular property F, it is not enough to simply write something on the order of "$\vee x \vee y$ (x is $F \wedge y$ is F)." The mere fact that the two *variables* 'x' and 'y' are different does not automatically entail that the statement is made true by two *distinct things*. Their difference must be addressed with an explicit addendum to the effect that they are *not* the same thing. For this purpose we require something on the order of "$\vee x \vee y$ (x is $F \wedge y$ is $F \wedge \neg(x=y)$)"; in the end, "$\vee x \vee y$ (x is $F \wedge y$ is F)" fails to go beyond "$\vee x$ (x is F)." But now suppose we want to say that there are *no more* than n objects (with property F). Then we would have to express the fact that whenever we encounter $n + 1$ objects $a_1, a_2, \ldots a_{n+1}$ with property F (or, more precisely, objects with $n + 1$ distinct *names*), they cannot all be pairwise distinct; behind at least two of their names hides one and the same object, such that either ($a_1 = a_2$, or $a_1 = a_3$, or $a_1 = a_4$, or . . . $a_1 = a_{n+1}$), or ($a_2 = a_3$, or . . . $a_2 = a_{n+1}$), or . . . or ($a_{n-1} = a_n$ or $a_{n-1} = a_{n+1}$), or ($a_n = a_{n+1}$). This state of affairs can also be described as follows: whenever we have n pairwise *distinct* objects $a_1, a_2, \ldots a_n$, any further object a_{n+1} (or, more precisely, any object with an additional *name*) must be identical with one of first n objects, so that either $a_{n+1} = a_1$, or $a_{n+1} = a_2$, or . . . $a_{n+1} = a_n$ (see solution to [b] below).

a. $\vee x \vee y \vee z$ (x is a democracy $\wedge$ y is a democracy $\wedge$ z is a democracy $\wedge \neg(x = y)$ $\wedge \neg(x = z) \wedge \neg(y = z)$)   Domain: states

b. $\vee x \vee y$ ($\neg(x = y) \wedge \wedge z$ ($z = x \vee z = y$))   Domain: sexes

Exercise 3.7

In the following solutions we will use "x likes y" in such a way as to treat x as corresponding to the grammatical subject, and y the direct object.

1. a likes $b \wedge b$ likes a
2. b likes $a \wedge \neg(a$ likes b)
3. $\neg(a$ likes a)
4. $\vee x$ (x likes a)   Domain: people
5. $\vee x \neg(x$ likes a)   Domain: people
6. $\wedge x \neg(a$ likes x)   Domain: people

7. $\wedge x(x$ likes $a)$ Domain: people
8. $\vee x \vee y$ $(x$ likes $y)$ Domain: people
9. $\wedge x \vee y$ $(x$ likes $y)$ Domain: people
10. $\vee x \wedge y$ $(y$ likes $x)$ Domain: people   (The solution given for [9] is also acceptable.)

11. $\neg \vee x \wedge y$ $(x$ likes $y)$ Domain: people   (Or: $\wedge x \neg \wedge y$ $(x$ likes $y)$)
12. $\vee x \neg \vee y$ $(y$ likes $x)$ Domain: people   (Or: $\vee x \wedge y \neg (y$ likes $x)$)
13. $\wedge x(x$ likes $x)$ Domain: people

Exercise 3.8

1. $\wedge x$ (Fred loves x)
   or,
   $\wedge x$ (x is an animal $\rightarrow$ Fred loves x)   Domain: animals / Domain: life forms
2. $\vee x$ (x is a mountain $\wedge \wedge y$ Domain: {mountains}
   (y is a person $\rightarrow$ y loves x)) $\cup$ {people}
3. $\neg \wedge x$ (x is a person $\rightarrow \vee y$ Domain: life forms
   (y is an animal $\wedge$ x loves y))
4. $\wedge x$ (x is a person $\wedge \wedge y$ (y is a car $\rightarrow x$ loves y) $\rightarrow x$ Domain: {cars}
   loves $x \wedge \wedge y$ (y is a car $\wedge$ y $\cup$ {people}
   belongs to $x \rightarrow x$ loves y))

This reading of (4) asserts that "every car lover loves not only him- or herself but also any cars belonging to him or her." If we also wish to add that every car lover has *exactly one* car, we must recall our discussion of Exercise 3.6. There we learned to express statements of the form "There is exactly one A, and this A has property B," in the following way:

$$\vee y (Ay \wedge \wedge z (Az \rightarrow z = y) \wedge By)$$

or more compactly,

$$\vee y (\wedge z (Az \leftrightarrow z = y) \wedge By)$$

Be sure to convince yourselves of the equivalence of the two formulations! With this addendum, (4) becomes:

$\bigwedge x$ (x is a person $\wedge$ $\bigwedge y$ (y is a car $\rightarrow$ x loves y) $\rightarrow$ 　　Domain: {cars}$\cup$
x loves x $\wedge$ $\bigvee y$ ($\bigwedge z$ (z is a car $\wedge$ z belongs to 　　{people}
$x \leftrightarrow z = y$) $\wedge$ x loves y))

Exercise 3.9.

This is a difficult exercise, with a great deal of interpretive wiggle room. As in Exercise 3.17, we must proceed by first considering the range of possible readings. In what follows, I have tried to pick the interpretations most amenable to treatment by means of the tools of predicate logic. Toward this end, I have generally picked fairly literal interpretations of proverbial utterances, none of which rules out other, equally literal interpretations. While they are not the only correct solutions, it is hoped that they will bear some resemblance to the widest *range* of correct solutions. In some cases, there were no obvious formalizable interpretations, and so the resulting glosses are highly unsatisfactory.

　　1. To begin with, we should note that the sentence "If wishes were horses, then beggars would ride," even when taken literally, as a statement about wishes, beggars, and horses, is a *counterfactual conditional.* In other words, its antecedent is *known* to be false (or contrary to fact—"counterfactual"). Unlike material conditionals, on whose formalization we have focused from the end of section II.1.1.d on, a counterfactual conditional is not automatically true when its antecedent is false—or all counterfactual conditionals would be true! Counterfactual conditionals are beyond our means, and so in formalizing this proverb, we have little choice but to read the "if . . . then" in sentence (1) as expressing a material conditional, something on the order of "If wishes are horses, then beggars ride."

　　Turning to the antecedent and consequent of this conditional, we confront a certain vagueness in the *quantity* of the statements "Wishes are horses" and "Beggars ride." What happens when we read both as existential?

$\bigvee x\, Hx \rightarrow \bigvee y\, (By \wedge Ry)$ 　　Domain$_x$: Wishes 　　Domain$_y$: People

where 'Hx' obviously stands for "x is a horse," 'By' for "y is a beggar," and 'Ry' for "y rides."

　　But this reading asserts that if there is some wish that is a horse, then some beggar rides, and this statement is true if only one beggar has been given a horse that he or she indeed uses for riding. Treating both antecedent and consequent as *universal* statements seems more in accord with the spirit of the proverb:

$$\wedge x\ Hx \rightarrow \wedge y\ (By \rightarrow Ry) \qquad \text{Domain}_x\text{: Wishes} \qquad \text{Domain}_y\text{: People}$$

Note that once we read the consequent of the conditional as universal, the embedded connective also becomes a conditional. "There is some F that is also G" requires a conjunctive predicate bound by an existential quantifier, while "All Fs are Gs" implies that for all x, if x is an F, then x is a G: a conditional structure.

If this reading is acceptable, we must bring it into line with the strictures of single-sorted predicate logic by performing the appropriate domain expansions. Defining $D = \{$wishes$\}\cup\{$people$\}$, and using the rule for domain expansion (section II.1.1.d.4), we obtain:

$$\wedge x\ (Wx \rightarrow Hx) \rightarrow \wedge y\ (By \rightarrow Ry) \qquad\qquad \text{Domain: D}$$

2. Franklin's aphorism—and, yes, it was coined by none other than Ben Franklin (1706–90), the American publisher, scientist, and inventor—poses a number of challenges, first among them being the familiar issue of quantity. How many pennies must be saved in order for a single penny to be earned? Is every penny saved a penny earned, or only the first one? Or the seventeenth? Or perhaps there is some particular penny that Franklin both saved and earned, one fine October morning in 1761, in a series of arduous negotiations with his Philadelphia paper stock supplier. But given that Franklin's general practice, in *Poor Richard's Almanack,* was to publish aphorisms thought to be of some general practical utility, it is unlikely he would have used this forum to boast of a successful business deal. He doubtless had a universal statement in mind. Let us interpret (2) as asserting that every penny that is saved is also a penny earned:

$$\wedge x\ (Px \rightarrow (Sx \rightarrow Ex)) \qquad\qquad \text{Domain}_x\text{: Monetary units}$$

where 'Px' stands for "x is a penny," 'Sx' for "x is saved," and 'Ex' for "x is earned."

What we have not addressed so far is the fact that being saved and being earned are not *properties* of pennies, or other monetary units, in and of themselves, but rather *relations* between such monetary units and the people who save and earn them. Further, Franklin's dictum concerns not one particular person, nor some extant but otherwise unspecified individual. It is, once again, a *universal* statement. Abbreviating "y is a human" as 'Hy', "y saves x" as 'Syx', "y earns x" as 'Eyx' and expanding our domain to $D = \{$monetary units$\}\cup\{$people$\}$, we obtain,

$$\wedge x \wedge y \,(Px \wedge Hy \rightarrow (Syx \rightarrow Eyx))$$ Domain: D

3. Following the lead set in our discussion of (2), we read "a man" in "Early to bed, early to rise, makes a man healthy, wealthy, and wise" as applying to *any* man, and we treat (3) as a *universal* statement. Furthermore, in the present-day context, the aphorism appears to apply to anyone who expends time (and labor) in pursuit of a wage, regardless of gender, and so we will read "man" as meaning "human being." The verb "makes" clearly expresses a *causal* relation of the kind which, as we have seen, the sort of logic we are dealing with here is ill-equipped to handle. We will substitute a conditional instead, formalizing the statement, "For any human *x*, if *x* is early to bed and early to rise, then *x* is healthy, wealthy, and wise."

$$\wedge x \,(Bx \wedge Rx \rightarrow Hx \wedge Wx \wedge Ix)$$ Domain: people

The abbreviations are self-evident. The intrinsic ambiguity of "early" is left unaddressed by this reading.

4. By now the problems of quantity are clear enough, though their solution, in this case, demands a somewhat different strategy. The statement expresses a relationship between human beings, apples, days, and doctors. Unpacking this relation, we discover a recipe for warding off doctors in general, and not some particular doctor. The physician-avoidance strategy does not, we assume, demand the consumption of exactly one apple a day. It may be supposed to work for *all* human beings and involve the consumption of *at least one* apple *every* day. Let '*Exyz*' stand for the three-place relation holding between a person, *x*, an apple, *y*, and a day, *z* such that *x* eats *y* on *z*, and '*Wxw*' for "*w* is kept away from *x*." Our first pass yields,

$$\wedge x(\wedge z \vee y\, Exyz \rightarrow \wedge w\, Wxw)$$
Domain$_x$ = People; Domain$_y$ = Apples; Domain$_z$ = Days; Domain$_w$ = Doctors

Some domain-expansion is clearly in order. We note that because {doctors}⊂ {people}, we need not expand the domain of variable *w*; we need only add a predicate, '*Ow*', for "*w* is a doctor." Let '*Hx*' stand for "*x* is a person," '*Ay*' for "*y* is an apple," '*Dz*' for "*z* is a day," and finally let D = {people}∪{apples}∪{days}. By our familiar rules for domain expansion, we obtain,

$$\wedge x \,(Hx \rightarrow (\wedge z \vee y\, (Ay \wedge Dz \wedge Exyz) \rightarrow \wedge w\, (Ow \rightarrow Wxw)))$$ Domain: D

A word on quantifier scope is in order. The universal quantifier with respect to x applies to the entire expression enclosed by the outermost pair of parentheses, whereas the remaining quantifiers are more restricted. Why? We recall that our general approach to statements of the form "All As are Bs" is to treat them as conditional expressions bound by universal quantifiers:

$$\bigwedge x\, (Ax \rightarrow Bx)$$

Despite its numerous complications, our reading of (4) retains this form. It is applying a property, the expression in the consequent of the embedded conditional, to all humans. This expression is also a conditional, intended to articulate, roughly, the idea that *if*, for every day, there is at least one apple, such that x eats the apple on that day, *then* doctors will avoid x. Put this way, it should be clear why the universal quantifier with respect to z and the existential quantifier with respect to y are placed as they are. Nor is their order interchangeable; consider the following:

$$\bigwedge x\, (Hx \rightarrow (\bigvee y \bigwedge z\, (Ay \wedge Dz \wedge Exyz) \rightarrow \bigwedge w\, (Ow \rightarrow Wxw))) \qquad \text{Domain: D}$$

This gloss, identical to our earlier effort except that the order of the quantifiers with respect to y and z is switched, imposes the following requirement: in order for me to successfully follow the prescribed physician-avoidance strategy, there must be some apple such that I eat that apple on every day. Now, surely it is possible for the consumption of an apple to span two days, especially if I take my first bite at 23:59:40 on one day, discarding the core on 00:03:23 on the following day. We might even envision scenarios in which an apple takes several days to eat. But clearly there can be no apple that is eaten on *every* day, nor is this what sentence (4) is meant to suggest. We retain our earlier reading.

5. The use of the masculine generic pronoun 'he' in this context can only imply that we have encountered yet another in the series of English devices for articulating universal statements. We should also be alert to possible readings of the article 'the' in 'the sword'. It seems plausible enough to unpack (5) as asserting that anyone who has a sword, and lives by it, dies by it, though clearly this reading (like all of our efforts) does violence to the underlying metaphor. Let 'Hx' stand for "x is a human," 'Sy' for "y is a sword," 'Axy' for "x has y," 'Lxy' for "x lives by y," and 'Dxy' for "x dies by y." With $D = \{\text{humans}\} \cup \{\text{swords}\}$, we obtain,

$$\bigwedge x\, (Hx \rightarrow (\bigwedge y (Sy \wedge Axy \wedge Lxy \rightarrow Dxy)) \qquad \text{Domain: D}$$

Equally plausibly, we might read the statement as asserting that for all humans x, if there is a sword by which x lives, then there is a sword (perhaps a different one) by which x dies. Employing the same predicates and domain, this reading becomes the following:

$$\bigwedge x(Hx \rightarrow (\bigvee y\ (Sy \wedge Axy \wedge Lxy) \rightarrow \bigvee z\ (Sz \wedge Dxy)))\qquad \text{Domain: D}$$

6. Despite its simplicity, this proverb is the most resistant to detailed logical analysis. To begin with, it clearly expresses a causal relation. Furthermore, it is irreducibly ambiguous in quantity (How many cats? Which ones? etc.). Perhaps we can come no closer than the following:

$$\bigvee x\ (Cx \wedge \bigvee y(Uxy \wedge Kyx))\qquad \text{Domain: D}$$

Where 'Cx' stands for "x is a cat," 'Uxy' for "x is curious about y," and 'Kyx' for "y killed x." For our domain, we choose D = {cats}∪{objects of curiosity}. This formalization asserts that there is a cat (x) who was curious about some y, such that y killed x. But then again, perhaps the proverb should be read as asserting that all curious cats are killed by their respective objects of curiosity. Using the same predicates and domain as before, we obtain,

$$\bigwedge x\ (Cx \rightarrow \bigwedge y\ (Uxy \rightarrow Kyx))\qquad \text{Domain: D}$$

Now we appear to be claiming that for all x, if x is a cat, then for all y, if x is curious about y, y kills x. The targeted reading is well captured.

One reason for our failure to adequately account for the quantity of this statement has to do with the logical status of the definite article 'the'. Logical systems whose complexity greatly exceeds that of our own have been devised to address the logic of so-called definite descriptions, with varying success.

Exercise 3.10

1. Show $\vDash \bigwedge z\ (Pz \vee \neg Pz)$. In this exercise, we proceed by analogy to the proof of the logical truth of Example 3.28. First, let any extensional interpretation of the formula be given, with any domain D. P_I, the extensionally interpreted predicate letter P, is assigned subset E_P of D as its extension. E_P contains exactly those elements of D to which P_I applies—i.e., for which $P_I z$ is true. (As these preliminaries remain nearly the same in all of the following proofs, they will henceforth be kept brief).

To prove the truth of $\wedge z(P_Iz \vee \neg P_Iz)$, we must demonstrate the truth of $P_Id \vee \neg P_Id$ for any arbitrary d in D. By selecting an *arbitrary* element d of D, we ensure that our arguments will apply equally well to *any* element of D, thus demonstrating the truth of $P_Id \vee \neg P_Id$ for any value of d, hence of $\wedge z(P_Iz \vee \neg P_Iz)$.

For $d \in D$, there are two possibilities:

1. $d \in E_P$. In that case, P_Id is true, and so $P_Id \vee \neg P_Id$ must also be true.

2. $d \notin E_P$. In that case, P_Id is false, so $\neg P_Id$ is true, and so $P_Id \vee \neg P_Id$ must also be true.

Since $P_Id \vee \neg P_Id$ is thus true for any arbitrary $d \in D$, the universal statement $\wedge z(P_Iz \vee \neg P_Iz)$ must be true; $\wedge z(Pz \vee \neg Pz)$ is true on this extensional interpretation. But since our choice of extensional interpretation was arbitrary, it follows that $\vDash \wedge z(Pz \vee \neg Pz)$. QED.

2. Show that $\vDash \wedge xFx \rightarrow \vee yFy$. Let an interpretation with non-empty domain D be given, such that E_F is the extension assigned to F. There are two possibilities:

1. $E_F = D$. Since D is non-empty, so is E_F. Then there is some $a \in E_F$, such that F_Ia is true. But then $\vee yF_Iy$ is true, hence $\wedge xF_Ix \rightarrow \vee yF_Iy$ is true.

2. $E_F \neq D$. Since $E_F \subset D$, there must be some $b \in D$ such that $b \notin E_F$, and for which F_Ib is false.

It follows that $\wedge xF_Ix$ is false, making $\wedge xF_Ix \rightarrow \vee yF_Iy$ true.

Having shown the truth of our formula under an arbitrarily chosen interpretation, we may conclude it to be true under *all* extensional interpretations, hence logically true. QED.

3. Show that $\vDash \wedge x(Tx \rightarrow Hx) \wedge Ts \rightarrow Hs$.

Let an interpretation be given in the usual way. We distinguish two possibilities:

1. $E_T \subset E_H$. Now consider some m_I, the element of D assigned to individual letter m under the given interpretation. Once again, there are two possibilities:

    a. $s_I \in E_T$. Since, by assumption, $E_T \subset E_H$, it follows that $s_I \in E_H$. So H_Is_I is true, as is $\wedge x (T_Ix \rightarrow H_Ix) \wedge T_Is_1 \rightarrow H_Is_I$.

    b. $m_I \notin E_D$. Then T_Is_I is false, so $\wedge x (T_Ix \rightarrow H_Ix) \wedge T_Is_I$ is false, and $\wedge(T_Ix \rightarrow H_Ix) \wedge T_Is_I \rightarrow H_Is_I$ is true.

2. $E_T \not\subseteq E_H$. Then there must be at least one $d \in D$ such that $d \in E_T$, but $d \notin E_H$. For this d, $T_I d$ is true and $H_I d$ false, making $T_I d \rightarrow H_I d$ false. In that case, $\wedge x\, (T_I x \rightarrow Hx)$ is false, and, as before, $\wedge x\, (T_I x \rightarrow H_I x) \wedge T_I s_I \rightarrow H_I s_I$ is true.

The conclusion that the formula in question is logically true follows in the usual way. QED.

4. Show that $\models \neg \wedge x Sx \leftrightarrow \vee x \neg Sx$. Let an interpretation be given in the usual way. We distinguish two possibilities:

1. $E_S \neq D$. There must then be a $b \in D$ such that $b \notin E_S$, in which case $S_I b$ is false. Then $\wedge x\, S_I x$ is false and $\neg S_I b$ is true, making both $\neg \wedge x S_I x$ and $\vee x \neg S_I x$ true.

2. $E_S = D$. Consider some arbitrary $a \in D$. By assumption, $a \in E_S$, making $S_I a$ true, $\neg S_I a$ false, and finally $\vee x \neg S_I x$ false, because a is an arbitrary element of D. By the identity of E_S with D, $S_I a$ must also be true for any a in D, and $\neg \wedge x S_I x$ false.

In both cases, the truth values of $\vee x \neg Sx$ and $\neg \wedge x S_I x$ coincide, so $\neg \wedge x S_I x \leftrightarrow \vee x \neg S_I x$ must be true, from which the claim to be proved follows. QED.

Exercise 3.11.

1. A and B are said to be predicate-logically contrary just in case $A \wedge B$ is PL-false.

2. A and B are said to be predicate-logically contradictory just in case $A \leftrightarrow B$ is PL-false.

3. A and B are said to be predicate-logically consistent just in case $A \wedge B$ is not PL-false.

4. A and B are said to be predicate-logically dependent just in case $A \models B$, or $B \models A$, or $A \models \neg B$, or $\neg B \models A$.

5. A is said to be predicate-logically necessary for B just in case $B \models A$.

6. A is said to be predicate-logically sufficient for B just in case $A \models B$.

Appendix 3 ✳ **Suggestions for Further Reading**

I need hardly mention that the following annotated list constitutes only a small sampling. Logic textbooks are as numerous as grains of sand and are written with the most diverse theoretical perspectives and pedagogical approaches. My selection thus emphasizes studies that either provide access to areas of logic not considered in the present book or more thorough treatments of particular topics. As for my fellow authors, who have turned directly to the bibliography in the hopes of finding their own works cited, I can only offer them my sincerest apologies if they come away disappointed; the book you hold in your hands is still worth its purchase price!

Boolos, George, J. P. Burgess, and R. Jeffrey. 2002. *Computability and Logic.* 4th ed. Cambridge: Cambridge University Press. This classic of mathematical logic, recently revised, has the virtue of demonstrating the important connections between formal logic and the theory of computation, or theoretical computer science. Problems given thorough treatment include the soundness and completeness of predicate logic, the *Entscheidungsproblem,* and Gödel's incompleteness theorems.

Edwards, Paul, ed. 1967. *The Encyclopedia of Philosophy.* New York: Macmillan. This has long been the standard English-language philosophical reference work. Useful articles on logic and related fields include "Definition," "Logic, History of," and "Logic, Modal" (for a discussion of strict implication). A more recent encyclopedia with many useful entries is Edward Craig, ed., *Routledge Encyclopedia of Philosophy* (London: Routledge, 1998). The *Stanford Encyclopedia of Philosophy,* a current online project, is also worth consulting (http://plato.stanford.edu/).

Haack, Susan. 1978. *Philosophy of Logics.* Cambridge: Cambridge University Press. A representative treatment of the philosophy of logic.

———. 1996. *Deviant Logic, Fuzzy Logic: Beyond the Formalism.* Chicago: University of Chicago Press. A philosophically oriented survey of "nonstandard" logics, including three-valued logics, paraconsistent logics, and others.

Hughes, R. I. G., ed. 1993. *A Philosophical Companion to First-Order Logic.* Indianapolis: Hacking. An anthology of essays providing points of entry into the philosophical problems of logic.

Kneale, William, and M. Kneale. 1975. *The Development of Logic.* Oxford: Clarendon. This standard history of logic also serves as an introduction to modern logic.

Mates, Benson. 1972. *Elementary Logic.* 2d ed. Oxford: Oxford University Press. While somewhat dated, this text still serves as the gold standard for mathematically oriented introductions to logic. It is thorough in its treatment of both proof and model theory, advancing as far as the proofs of the soundness and completeness of first-order predicate logic.

Read, Stephen. 1988. *Relevant Logic: A Philosophical Examination of Inference.* Oxford: Blackwell. This book presents attempts, based on the logic of relevance, to overcome the weaknesses of classical statement logic arising out of the use of the conditional in explicating valid inference.

———. 1994. *Thinking about Logic: An Introduction to the Philosophy of Logic.* Oxford: Oxford University Press.

Strawson, Peter F. 1952. *Introduction to Logical Theory.* London: Methuen. Another classic in the philosophy of logic.

Wolfram, Sybil. 1989. *Philosophical Logic: An Introduction.* London: Routledge. An introduction to the most salient philosophical problems of logic.